Of Mice and Men

Herausgegeben von
Reinhard Gratzke

Philipp Reclam jun. Stuttgart

Diese Ausgabe darf nur in der Bundesrepublik Deutschland, in Österreich und in der Schweiz vertrieben werden.

This edition may only be sold in Germany, Austria and Switzerland.

Umschlagabbildung: Szene aus dem gleichnamigen Film mit John Malkovich und Gary Sinise, Regie: Gary Sinise (Foto: United International Pictures)

RECLAMS UNIVERSAL-BIBLIOTHEK Nr. 9253
Alle Rechte vorbehalten
Copyright für diese Ausgabe
© 1989 Philipp Reclam jun. GmbH & Co. KG, Stuttgart
Copyright für den Text
© 1937, 1965 John Steinbeck. Abdruck mit Genehmigung von
Elaine A. Steinbeck c/o McIntosh and Otis, Inc., New York
Bibliographisch ergänzte Ausgabe 2003
Gesamtherstellung: Reclam, Ditzingen. Printed in Germany 2012
RECLAM, UNIVERSAL-BIBLIOTHEK und RECLAMS
UNIVERSAL-BIBLIOTHEK sind eingetragene Marken
der Philipp Reclam jun. GmbH & Co. KG, Stuttgart
ISBN 978-3-15-009253-8

www.reclam.de

Of Mice and Men

One

A few miles south of Soledad, the Salinas River drops in
close to the hillside bank and runs deep and green. The
water is warm too, for it has slipped twinkling over the
yellow sands in the sunlight before reaching the narrow
pool. On one side of the river the golden foothill slopes
curve up to the strong and rocky Gabilan Mountains,
but on the valley side the water is lined with trees –
willows fresh and green with every spring, carrying in
their lower leaf junctures the debris of the winter's
flooding; and sycamores with mottled, white, recumbent limbs and branches that arch over the pool. On the
sandy bank under the trees the leaves lie deep and so
crisp that a lizard makes a great skittering if he runs

3 **Soledad:** Ort im mittleren Kalifornien, etwa 200 km südlich von San
   Francisco im Tal des Salinas River gelegen, einer auch heute noch
   hauptsächlich landwirtschaftlich strukturierten Gegend.
7 **foothill:** Gebirgsausläufer.
8 **Gabilan Mountains** (pl.): zum Salinas-Tal paralleler Gebirgszug.
11 **leaf junctures:** Blattverzweigungen.
   debris: hier: Reste, Überbleibsel.
12 **sycamore:** nordamerikanische Platane.
   mottled: gesprenkelt, fleckig.
12f. **recumbent:** ruhend, liegend.
13 **limb:** Ast.
   to arch over s.th.: sich über etwas wölben.
15 **crisp:** trocken (Blätter).
   lizard: Eidechse.
   skittering: leichtfüßiges Huschen, Trippeln.

3

among them. Rabbits come out of the brush to sit on the
sand in the evening, and the damp flats are covered with
the night tracks of 'coons, and with the spread pads of
dogs from the ranches, and with the split-wedge tracks
5 of deer that come to drink in the dark.
There is a path through the willows and among the
sycamores, a path beaten hard by boys coming down
from the ranches to swim in the deep pool, and beaten
hard by tramps who come wearily down from the high-
10 way in the evening to jungle-up near water. In front of
the low horizontal limb of a giant sycamore there is an
ash pile made by many fires; the limb is worn smooth by
men who have sat on it.

Evening of a hot day started the little wind to moving
15 among the leaves. The shade climbed up the hills
toward the top. On the sand banks the rabbits sat as
quietly as little gray sculptured stones. And then from
the direction of the state highway came the sound of
footsteps on crisp sycamore leaves. The rabbits hurried
20 noiselessly for cover. A stilted heron labored up into the
air and pounded down river. For a moment the place

---

1 **brush:** Unterholz.
3 **'coon:** Kurzform von *racoon:* Waschbär.
  pad: Fußabdruck, Spur.
4 **ranch** (AE): (Vieh-)Farm.
  split-wedge: keilförmig gespalten (*wedge:* Keil).
10 **to jungle-up** (slang): ein provisorisches Nachtlager im Freien aufschlagen (in bezug auf Landstreicher gebraucht).
11 **horizontal:** waagrecht.
17 **sculptured:** behauen.
20 **cover:** Deckung, Schutz.
  stilted: gestelzt.
  heron: Reiher.
21 **to pound:** schwer (auf)schlagen.

was lifeless, and then two men emerged from the path
and came into the opening by the green pool.

They had walked in single file down the path, and even
in the open one stayed behind the other. Both were
5 dressed in denim trousers and in denim coats with brass
buttons. Both wore black, shapeless hats and both
carried tight blanket rolls slung over their shoulders.
The first man was small and quick, dark of face, with
restless eyes and sharp, strong features. Every part of
10 him was defined: small, strong hands, slender arms, a
thin and bony nose. Behind him walked his opposite, a
huge man, shapeless of face, with large, pale eyes,
and wide, sloping shoulders; and he walked heavily,
dragging his feet a little, the way a bear drags his
15 paws. His arms did not swing at his sides, but hung
loosely.

The first man stopped short in the clearing, and the
follower nearly ran over him. He took off his hat and
wiped the sweat-band with his forefinger and snapped
20 the moisture off. His huge companion dropped his
blankets and flung himself down and drank from the
surface of the green pool; drank with long gulps, snort-
ing into the water like a horse. The small man stepped
nervously beside him.

---

3 **in single file:** im Gänsemarsch, hintereinander.
5 **denim:** Jeansstoff, Köper.
7 **to sling:** (über die Schulter) hängen.
10 **defined:** bestimmt.
   slender: schlank.
14 **to drag:** nachziehen.
17 **to stop short:** abrupt stehenbleiben.
19 **to snap:** schnipsen.
22 **gulp:** gieriger Schluck.
22 f. **to snort:** schnauben.

"Lennie!" he said sharply. "Lennie, for God' sakes don't drink so much." Lennie continued to snort into the pool. The small man leaned over and shook him by the shoulder. "Lennie. You gonna be sick like you was last night."

Lennie dipped his whole head under, hat and all, and then he sat up on the bank and his hat dripped down on his blue coat and ran down his back. "That's good," he said. "You drink some, George. You take a good big drink." He smiled happily.

George unslung his bindle and dropped it gently on the bank. "I ain't sure it's good water," he said. "Looks kinda scummy."

Lennie dabbled his big paw in the water and wiggled his fingers so the water arose in little splashes; rings widened across the pool to the other side and came back again. Lennie watched them go. "Look, George. Look what I done."

George knelt beside the pool and drank from his hand with quick scoops. "Tastes all right," he admitted. "Don't really seem to be running, though. You never

---

1 **for God' sakes** (dial.): *for God's sake:* hier: verärgerter Ausruf; Herrgott nochmal!

4 **you gonna** (slang): *you are going to.*

12 **ain't** (infml.): *am not* (im folgenden häufig als Ersatz für alle Formen von *to be not* und *to have not* gebraucht).

13 **kinda** (dial.): *kind of:* ein bißchen, irgendwie.

    scummy: mit einer grünen Schleimschicht bedeckt (stehendes Gewässer).

14 **to dabble:** (im Wasser) planschen.

    to wiggle: wackeln.

15 **splash:** Spritzer.

20 **scoop:** Schöpfbewegung.

oughta drink water when it ain't running, Lennie," he
said hopelessly. "You'd drink out of a gutter if you was
thirsty." He threw a scoop of water into his face and
rubbed it about with his hand, under his chin and
5 around the back of his neck. Then he replaced his hat,
pushed himself back from the river, drew up his knees
and embraced them. Lennie, who had been watching,
imitated George exactly. He pushed himself back, drew
up his knees, embraced them, looked over to George
10 to see whether he had it just right. He pulled his hat
down a little more over his eyes, the way George's hat
was.

George stared morosely at the water. The rims of his
eyes were red with sun glare. He said angrily, "We
15 could just as well of rode clear to the ranch if that
bastard bus driver knew what he was talkin' about. 'Jes'
a little stretch down the highway,' he says. 'Jes' a little
stretch.' God damn near four miles, that's what it was!
Didn't wanta stop at the ranch gate, that's what. Too
20 God damn lazy to pull up. Wonder he isn't too damn
good to stop in Soledad at all. Kicks us out and says 'Jes'

---

1 **oughta** (dial.): *ought to.*
2 **gutter:** Rinnstein, Gosse.
13 **morosely** (adv.): verdrießlich, mißmutig.
   rim: Rand.
15 **of** (dial.): *have.*
   clear (AE, infml.): hier: geradewegs.
16 **bastard** (slang): Bastard, Hundesohn (starkes Schimpfwort, das im
   folgenden aber auch freundschaftlich gebraucht wird).
   jes' (auch: *jus'*) (dial.): *just.*
18 **God damn** (infml.): (gott-)verdammt.
19 **that's what** (infml.): so sieht's aus.
20 **to pull up:** (am Straßenrand) anhalten (AE).
   wonder (infml.): *it's a wonder.*

a little stretch down the road.' I bet it was *more* than
four miles. Damn hot day."
Lennie looked timidly over to him. "George?"
"Yeah, what ya want?"
5 "Where we goin', George?"
The little man jerked down the brim of his hat and
scowled over at Lennie. "So you forgot that awready,
did you? I gotta tell you again, do I? Jesus Christ,
you're a crazy bastard!"
10 "I forgot," Lennie said softly. "I tried not to forget.
Honest to God I did, George."
"O.K. – O.K. I'll tell ya again. I ain't got nothing to do.
Might jus' as well spen' all my time tellin' you things and
then you forget 'em, and I tell you again."
15 "Tried and tried," said Lennie, "but it didn't do no
good. I remember about the rabbits, George."
"The hell with the rabbits. That's all you ever can
remember is them rabbits. O.K.! Now you listen and
this time you got to remember so we don't get in no
20 trouble. You remember settin' in that gutter on Howard
Street and watchin' that blackboard?"
Lennie's face broke into a delighted smile. "Why sure,

4 **what ya want?** (slang): *what do you want?*
6 **to jerk:** hier: ruckartig ziehen.
   brim: (Hut-)Rand.
7 **to scowl:** finster blicken.
   awready (dial.): *already.*
8 **I gotta** (infml.): *I've got to.*
   Jesus Christ (infml.): Kraftausdruck; etwa: Kruzifix!
11 **honest to God:** Ehrenwort!
14 **'em** (auch: *'um*) (dial.): *them.*
17 **the hell with ...** (infml.): zum Teufel mit ...
18 **them** (dial.): *those.*
20 **to set** (AE, infml.): *sit.*

8

George. I remember that ... but ... what'd we do
then? I remember some girls come by and you says ...
you says ..."

"The hell with what I says. You remember about us
goin' in to Murray and Ready's, and they give us work
cards and bus tickets?"

"Oh, sure, George. I remember that now." His hands
went quickly into his side coat pockets. He said gently,
"George ... I ain't got mine. I musta lost it." He looked
down at the ground in despair.

"You never had none, you crazy bastard. I got both of
'em here. Think I'd let you carry your own work
card?"

Lennie grinned with relief. "I ... I thought I put it in my
side pocket." His hand went into the pocket again.

George looked sharply at him. "What'd you take outa
that pocket?"

"Ain't a thing in my pocket." Lennie said cleverly.

"I know there ain't. You got it in your hand. What you
got in your hand – hidin' it?"

"I ain't got nothin', George. Honest."

"Come on, give it here."

Lennie held his closed hand away from George's direction. "It's on'y a mouse, George."

"A mouse? A live mouse?"

"Uh-uh. Jus' a dead mouse, George. I didn't kill it.
Honest! I found it. I found it dead."

"Give it here!" said George.

"Aw, leave me have it, George."

---

5 **Murray and Ready's:** private Arbeitsvermittlungsagentur.

5f. **work card:** Vermittlungsnachweis, Arbeitsbuch.

9 **musta** (dial.): *must have.*

29 **to leave:** *let* (AE).

"Give it here!"

Lennie's closed hand slowly obeyed. George took the mouse and threw it across the pool to the other side, among the brush. "What you want of a dead mouse, anyways?"

"I could pet it with my thumb while we walked along," said Lennie.

"Well, you ain't petting no mice while you walk with me. You remember where we're goin' now?"

Lennie looked startled and then in embarrassment hid his face against his knees. "I forgot again."

"Jesus Christ," George said resignedly. "Well – look, we're gonna work on a ranch like the one we come from up north."

"Up north?"

"In Weed."

"Oh, sure. I remember. In Weed."

"That ranch we're goin' to is right down there about a quarter mile. We're gonna go in an' see the boss. Now, look – I'll give him the work tickets, but you ain't gonna say a word. You jus' stand there and don't say nothing. If he finds out what a crazy bastard you are, we won't get no job, but if he sees ya work before he hears ya talk, we're set. Ya got that?"

"Sure, George. Sure I got it."

"O.K. Now when we go in to see the boss, what you gonna do?"

---

6 **to pet:** tätscheln, streicheln, liebkosen.

10 **embarrassment:** Verlegenheit.

12 **resignedly** (adv.): (sich mit etwas) abfindend.

16 **Weed:** Ort in Nordkalifornien, nahe dem Ursprung des Sacramento, fast 600 km von Soledad entfernt.

24 **to be set** (infml.): es geschafft haben.

"I ... I ..." Lennie thought. His face grew tight with thought. "I ... ain't gonna say nothin'. Jus' gonna stan' there."

"Good boy. That's swell. You say that over two, three
5 times so you sure won't forget it."

Lennie droned to himself softly, "I ain't gonna say nothin' ... I ain't gonna say nothin' ... I ain't gonna say nothin'."

"O.K.," said George. "An' you ain't gonna do no bad
10 things like you done in Weed, neither."

Lennie looked puzzled. "Like I done in Weed?"

"Oh, so ya forgot that too, did ya? Well, I ain't gonna remind ya, fear ya do it again."

A light of understanding broke on Lennie's face. "They
15 run us outa Weed," he exploded triumphantly.

"Run us out, hell," said George disgustedly. "We run. They was lookin' for us, but they didn't catch us."

Lennie giggled happily. "I didn't forget that, you bet."

20 George lay back on the sand and crossed his hands under his head, and Lennie imitated him, raising his head to see whether he was doing it right. "God, you're a lot of trouble," said George. "I could get along so easy and so nice if I didn't have you on my tail. I could live so
25 easy and maybe have a girl."

For a moment Lennie lay quiet, and then he said hopefully, "We gonna work on a ranch, George."

---

4 **swell** (infml.): klasse, toll.
6 **to drone:** hier: (herunter)leiern.
15 **to run s.o. out** (infml.): jdn. vertreiben, zum Teufel jagen.
18 **to giggle:** kichern.
18f. **you bet** (infml.): darauf kannst du wetten.
24 **to have s.o. on one's tail** (slang): jdn. am Rockzipfel hängen haben.

"Awright. You got that. But we're gonna sleep here because I got a reason."

The day was going fast now. Only the tops of the Gabilan Mountains flamed with the light of the sun that had gone from the valley. A water snake slipped along on the pool, its head held up like a little periscope. The reeds jerked slightly in the current. Far off toward the highway a man shouted something, and another man shouted back. The sycamore limbs rustled under a little wind that died immediately.

"George – why ain't we goin' on to the ranch and get some supper? They got supper at the ranch."

George rolled on his side. "No reason at all for you. I like it here. Tomorra we're gonna go to work. I seen thrashin' machines on the way down. That means we'll be bucking grain bags, bustin' a gut. Tonight I'm gonna lay right here and look up. I like it."

Lennie got up on his knees and looked down at George. "Ain't we gonna have no supper?"

"Sure we are, if you gather up some dead willow sticks. I got three cans of beans in my bindle. You get a fire ready. I'll give you a match when you get the sticks together. Then we'll heat the beans and have supper."

Lennie said, "I like beans with ketchup."

---

6 **periscope:** Periskop (Sehrohr bei U-Booten).
7 **to jerk:** (sich) ruckartig bewegen.
15 **thrashing machine:** Dreschmaschine.
16 **to buck grain bags** (infml.): Getreidesäcke auf- oder abladen.
   to bust a gut (slang): sich zu Tode schinden; eigtl.: sich einen Bruch heben.
21 **bindle** (slang): in einer Decke zusammengerollte Habseligkeiten.

12

"Well, we ain't got no ketchup. You go get wood. An' don't you fool around. It'll be dark before long."

Lennie lumbered to his feet and disappeared in the brush. George lay where he was and whistled softly to himself. There were sounds of splashings down the river in the direction Lennie had taken. George stopped whistling and listened. "Poor bastard," he said softly, and then went on whistling again.

In a moment Lennie came crashing back through the brush. He carried one small willow stick in his hand. George sat up. "Awright," he said brusquely. "Gi'me that mouse!"

But Lennie made an elaborate pantomime of innocence. "What mouse, George? I ain't got no mouse."

George held out his hand. "Come on. Give it to me. You ain't puttin' nothing over."

Lennie hesitated, backed away, looked wildly at the brush line as though he contemplated running for his freedom. George said coldly, "You gonna give me that mouse or do I have to sock you?"

"Give you what, George?"

"You know God damn well what. I want that mouse."

---

2 **to fool around** (infml.): herumalbern.
3 **to lumber to one's feet** (infml.): schwerfällig aufstehen, sich hochrappeln.
11 **brusquely** (adv.): brüsk, schroff.
   gi'me (infml.): *give me.*
13 **elaborate:** hier: umständlich, übertrieben, wohleinstudiert.
   pantomime: Pantomime, gestische Darstellung.
   innocence: Unschuld.
16 **to put s.th. over** (*on s.o.*) (slang): jdn. mit etwas reinlegen, übervorteilen, linken.
20 **to sock s.o.** (slang): jdm. eine verpassen, jdn. hauen.

Lennie reluctantly reached into his pocket. His voice broke a little. "I don't know why I can't keep it. It ain't nobody's mouse. I didn't steal it. I found it lyin' right beside the road."

5 George's hand remained outstretched imperiously. Slowly, like a terrier who doesn't want to bring a ball to its master, Lennie approached, drew back, approached again. George snapped his fingers sharply, and at the sound Lennie laid the mouse in his hand.

10 "I wasn't doin' nothing bad with it, George. Jus' strokin' it."

George stood up and threw the mouse as far as he could into the darkening brush, and then he stepped to the pool and washed his hands. "You crazy fool. Don't you 15 think I could see your feet was wet where you went acrost the river to get it?" He heard Lennie's whimpering cry and wheeled about. "Blubberin' like a baby! Jesus Christ! A big guy like you." Lennie's lip quivered and tears started in his eyes. "Aw, Lennie!" George put 20 his hand on Lennie's shoulder. "I ain't takin' it away jus' for meanness. That mouse ain't fresh, Lennie; and besides, you've broke it pettin' it. You get another mouse that's fresh and I'll let you keep it a little while."

25 Lennie sat down on the ground and hung his head

---

1 **reluctantly** (adv.): widerwillig, widerstrebend.
2 **to break:** hier: stocken.
5 **imperiously** (adv.): gebieterisch.
16 **acrost:** *across.*
16f. **whimpering:** wimmernd.
17 **to blubber** (slang): flennen, heulen.
18 **guy** (AE, infml.): Kerl, Bursche, Typ.

dejectedly. "I don't know where there is no other mouse. I remember a lady used to give 'em to me – ever'one she got. But that lady ain't here."

George scoffed. "Lady, huh? Don't even remember
5 who that lady was. That was your own Aunt Clara. An' she stopped givin' 'em to ya. You always killed 'em."

Lennie looked sadly up at him. "They was so little," he said, apologetically. "I'd pet 'em, and pretty soon they bit my fingers and I pinched their heads a little and then
10 they was dead – because they was so little.

"I wisht we'd get the rabbits pretty soon, George. They ain't so little."

"The hell with the rabbits. An' you ain't to be trusted with no live mice. Your Aunt Clara give you a rubber
15 mouse and you wouldn't have nothing to do with it."

"It wasn't no good to pet," said Lennie.

The flame of the sunset lifted from the mountaintops and dusk came into the valley, and a half darkness came in among the willows and the sycamores. A big carp
20 rose to the surface of the pool, gulped air and then sank mysteriously into the dark water again, leaving widening rings on the water. Overhead the leaves whisked again and little puffs of willow cotton blew down and landed on the pool's surface.

---

1 **dejectedly** (adv.): niedergeschlagen, deprimiert.
2f. **ever'one** (slang): *everyone.*
4 **to scoff:** abschätzig bemerken, spotten.
8 **apologetically** (adv.): entschuldigend, bedauernd.
11 **wisht** (dial.): *wished.*
19 **carp:** Karpfen.
20 **to gulp air:** gierig nach Luft schnappen.
22 **to whisk:** hier: im Wind rauschen.
23 **puffs of willow cotton** (pl.): Büschel von Weidenwolle.

"You gonna get that wood?" George demanded.
"There's plenty right up against the back of that sycamore. Floodwater wood. Now you get it."

Lennie went behind the tree and brought out a litter
5 of dried leaves and twigs. He threw them in a heap on
the old ash pile and went back for more and more. It
was almost night now. A dove's wings whistled over
the water. George walked to the fire pile and lighted
the dry leaves. The flame cracked up among the twigs
10 and fell to work. George undid his bindle and brought
out three cans of beans. He stood them about the fire,
close in against the blaze, but not quite touching the
flame.

"There's enough beans for four men," George said.

15 Lennie watched him from over the fire. He said
patiently, "I like 'em with ketchup."

"Well, we ain't got any," George exploded. "Whatever
we ain't got, that's what you want. God a'mighty, if I
was alone I could live so easy. I could go get a job an'
20 work, an' no trouble. No mess at all, and when the end
of the month come I could take my fifty bucks and go
into town and get whatever I want. Why, I could stay in
a cat house all night. I could eat any place I want, hotel
or any place, and order any damn thing I could think of.
25 An' I could do all that every damn month. Get a gallon

---

4 **litter:** Haufen.
9 **to crack up:** aufprasseln.
10 **to fall to work:** sich an die Arbeit machen.
11 **to stand** (AE, infml.): hier: (hin)stellen.
20 **no mess at all** (slang): nicht die Spur von 'nem Schlamassel.
21 **buck** (slang): Dollar.
23 **cat house** (slang): Puff, Bordell.
25 **gallon:** Gallone (Hohlmaß, 3,785 l).

16

of whisky, or set in a pool room and play cards or shoot pool." Lennie knelt and looked over the fire at the angry George. And Lennie's face was drawn with terror. "An' whatta I got," George went on furiously. "I got you! You can't keep a job and you lose me ever' job I get. Jus' keep me shovin' all over the country all the time. An' that ain't the worst. You get in trouble. You do bad things and I got to get you out." His voice rose nearly to a shout. "You crazy son-of-a-bitch. You keep me in hot water all the time." He took on the elaborate manner of little girls when they are mimicking one another. "Jus' wanted to feel that girl's dress – jus' wanted to pet it like it was a mouse — Well, how the hell did she know you jus' wanted to feel her dress? She jerks back and you hold on like it was a mouse. She yells and we got to hide in a irrigation ditch all day with guys lookin' for us, and we got to sneak out in the dark and

---

1 **pool room** (infml.): Billardraum; *pool* bezeichnet mehrere Varianten von Billard, bei denen 15 Kugeln in sechs Taschen am Rand des Tisches versenkt werden; in den USA meist mit Geldeinsatz verbunden.
 to shoot (infml.): hier: spielen (d. h. mit dem Queue stoßen).
3 f. **drawn with terror:** schreckverzerrt.
4 **whatta** (dial.): *what have.*
6 **to shove all over the country** (slang): sich durch das ganze Land placken.
9 **son-of-a-bitch** (slang): Hurensohn; wie *bastard* auf dieser Stilebene oft auch freundschaftlich oder als Mittel der Emphase gebraucht, vgl. S. 126, Z. 20 das adverbial verwendete *son-of-a-bitching* (*bitch:* Hure).
9 f. **to keep s.o. in hot water** (infml.): jdn. ständig in Schwierigkeiten bringen.
11 **to mimic:** nachahmen, nachäffen.
16 **irrigation ditch:** Bewässerungsgraben.
17 **to sneak out** (infml.): hinausschleichen, sich davonmachen.

get outa the country. All the time somethin' like that –
all the time. I wisht I could put you in a cage with about
a million mice an' let you have fun." His anger left
him suddenly. He looked across the fire at Lennie's
anguished face, and then he looked ashamedly at the
flames.

It was quite dark now, but the fire lighted the trunks of
the trees and the curving branches overhead. Lennie
crawled slowly and cautiously around the fire until he
was close to George. He sat back on his heels. George
turned the bean cans so that another side faced the fire.
He pretended to be unaware of Lennie so close beside
him.

"George," very softly. No answer. "George!"

"Whatta you want?"

"I was only foolin', George. I don't want no ketchup. I
wouldn't eat no ketchup if it was right here beside
me."

"If it was here, you could have some."

"But I wouldn't eat none, George. I'd leave it all for
you. You could cover your beans with it and I wouldn't
touch none of it."

George still stared morosely at the fire. "When I think
of the swell time I could have without you, I go nuts. I
never get no peace."

Lennie still knelt. He looked off into the darkness
across the river. "George, you want I should go away
and leave you alone?"

"Where the hell could you go?"

---

5 **anguished:** qualvoll.
15 **whatta** (dial.): *what do.*
24 **to go nuts** (slang): verrückt werden, durchdrehen.

"Well, I could. I could go off in the hills there. Some place I'd find a cave."

"Yeah? How'd you eat? You ain't got sense enough to find nothing to eat."

5 "I'd find things, George. I don't need no nice food with ketchup. I'd lay out in the sun and nobody'd hurt me. An' if I foun' a mouse, I could keep it. Nobody'd take it away from me."

George looked quickly and searchingly at him. "I been
10 mean, ain't I?"

"If you don' want me I can go off in the hills an' find a cave. I can go away any time."

"No – look! I was jus' foolin', Lennie. 'Cause I want you to stay with me. Trouble with mice is you always kill
15 'em." He paused. "Tell you what I'll do, Lennie. First chance I get I'll give you a pup. Maybe you wouldn't kill *it*. That'd be better than mice. And you could pet it harder."

Lennie avoided the bait. He had sensed his advantage.
20 "If you don't want me, you only jus' got to say so, and I'll go off in those hills right there – right up in those hills and live by myself. An' I won't get no mice stole from me."

George said, "I want you to stay with me, Lennie. Jesus
25 Christ, somebody'd shoot you for a coyote if you was by yourself. No, you stay with me. Your Aunt Clara wouldn't like you running off by yourself, even if she is dead."

---

3 **sense:** Verstand.
16 **pup:** Kurzform von *puppy:* Welpe.
19 **bait:** Köder.
25 **coyote:** Kojote, nordamerikanischer Präriewolf.

Lennie spoke craftily, "Tell me – like you done before."

"Tell you what?"

"About the rabbits."

5 George snapped, "You ain't gonna put nothing over on me."

Lennie pleaded, "Come on, George. Tell me. Please, George. Like you done before."

"You get a kick outa that, don't you? Awright, I'll tell
10 you, and then we'll eat our supper ..."

George's voice became deeper. He repeated his words rhythmically as though he had said them many times before. "Guys like us, that work on ranches, are the loneliest guys in the world. They got no fambly. They
15 don't belong no place. They come to a ranch an' work up a stake and then they go into town and blow their stake, and the first thing you know they're poundin' their tail on some other ranch. They ain't got nothing to look ahead to."

20 Lennie was delighted. "That's it – that's it. Now tell how it is with us."

George went on. "With us it ain't like that. We got a future. We got somebody to talk to that gives a damn about us. We don't have to sit in no bar room blowin' in
25 our jack jus' because we got no place else to go. If them

---

1 **craftily** (adv.): bauernschlau, listig.
9 **to get a kick out of s.th.** (slang): auf etwas ‚abfahren‘, von etwas in höchste Erregung versetzt werden.
14 **fambly** (dial.): *family*.
16 **stake** (slang): größere Summe von Erspartem.
   to blow (slang): verjubeln, auf den Kopf hauen.
17 f. **to pound one's tail** (slang): sich abrackern, abschuften.
24 f. **to blow in one's jack** (slang): sein Geld verpulvern.

20

other guys gets in jail they can rot for all anybody gives a damn. But not us."

Lennie broke in. *"But not us! An' why? Because ... because I got you to look after me, and you got me to*
5 *look after you, and that's why."* He laughed delightedly. "Go on now, George!"

"You got it by heart. You can do it yourself."

"No, you. I forget some a' the things. Tell about how it's gonna be."

10 "O.K. Someday – we're gonna get the jack together and we're gonna have a little house and a couple of acres an' a cow and some pigs and —"

"An' live off the fatta the lan'," Lennie shouted. "An' have *rabbits*. Go on, George! Tell about what we're
15 gonna have in the garden and about the rabbits in the cages and about the rain in the winter and the stove, and how thick the cream is on the milk like you can hardly cut it. Tell about that, George."

"Why'n't you do it yourself? You know all of it."

20 "No ... you tell it. It ain't the same if I tell it. Go on ... George. How I get to tend the rabbits."

"Well," said George, "we'll have a big vegetable patch and a rabbit hutch and chickens. And when it rains in the winter, we'll just say the hell with goin' to work, and
25 we'll build up a fire in the stove and set around it an' listen to the rain comin' down on the roof – Nuts!" He

---

1 f. **to give a damn** (slang): sich einen Dreck (um etwas) scheren.

8 **some a'** (dial.): *some of.*

13 **to live off the fat of the land:** etwa: wie Gott in Frankreich leben; die Redewendung geht zurück auf 1. Mose 45,18: »[...] und ihr sollt das Fett des Landes essen« (gemeint ist Kanaan, das Gelobte Land).

19 **why'n't** (dial.): *why don't.*

23 **hutch:** Verschlag, Stall.

took out his pocket knife. "I ain't got time for no more." He drove his knife through the top of one of the bean cans, sawed out the top and passed the can to Lennie. Then he opened a second can. From his side pocket he brought out two spoons and passed one of them to Lennie.

They sat by the fire and filled their mouths with beans and chewed mightily. A few beans slipped out of the side of Lennie's mouth. George gestured with his spoon. "What you gonna say tomorrow when the boss asks you questions?"

Lennie stopped chewing and swallowed. His face was concentrated. "I ... I ain't gonna ... say a word."

"Good boy! That's fine, Lennie! Maybe you're gettin' better. When we get the coupla acres I can let you tend the rabbits all right. 'Specially if you remember as good as that."

Lennie choked with pride. "I can remember," he said.

George motioned with his spoon again. "Look, Lennie. I want you to look around here. You can remember this place, can't you? The ranch is about a quarter mile up that way. Just follow the river?"

"Sure," said Lennie. "I can remember this. Di'n't I remember about not gonna say a word?"

"'Course you did. Well, look. Lennie – if you jus' happen to get in trouble like you always done before, I want you to come right here an' hide in the brush."

"Hide in the brush," said Lennie slowly.

---

9 **to gesture:** gestikulieren.
26 **'course** (dial.): *of course*.

"Hide in the brush till I come for you. Can you remember that?"

"Sure I can, George. Hide in the brush till you come."

5 "But you ain't gonna get in no trouble, because if you do, I won't let you tend the rabbits." He threw his empty bean can off into the brush.

"I won't get in no trouble, George. I ain't gonna say a word."

10 "O.K. Bring your bindle over here by the fire. It's gonna be nice sleepin' here. Lookin' up, and the leaves. Don't build up no more fire. We'll let her die down."

They made their beds on the sand, and as the blaze
15 dropped from the fire the sphere of light grew smaller; the curling branches disappeared and only a faint glimmer showed where the tree trunks were. From the darkness Lennie called, "George – you asleep?"

"No. Whatta you want?"

20 "Let's have different color rabbits, George."

"Sure we will," George said sleepily. "Red and blue and green rabbits, Lennie. Millions of 'em."

"Furry ones, George, like I seen in the fair in Sacramento."

25 "Sure, furry ones."

"'Cause I can jus' as well go away, George, an' live in a cave."

"You can jus' as well go to hell," said George. "Shut up now."

---

12 **her** (dial.): *it.*
15 **sphere:** Kreis.
23 f. **Sacramento:** Hauptstadt Kaliforniens.

The red light dimmed on the coals. Up the hill from the river a coyote yammered, and a dog answered from the other side of the stream. The sycamore leaves whispered in a little night breeze.

5 Two

The bunkhouse was a long, rectangular building. Inside, the walls were whitewashed and the floor unpainted. In three walls there were small, square windows, and in the fourth, a solid door with a wooden latch. Against
10 the walls were eight bunks, five of them made up with blankets and the other three showing their burlap ticking. Over each bunk there was nailed an apple box with the opening forward so that it made two shelves for the personal belongings of the occupant of the bunk. And
15 these shelves were loaded with little articles, soap and talcum powder, razors and those Western magazines ranch men love to read and scoff at and secretly believe. And there were medicines on the shelves, and little vials, combs; and from nails on the box sides, a few
20 neckties. Near one wall there was a black cast-iron stove, its stovepipe going straight up through the ceil-

---

2 **to yammer:** jammern.
6 **bunkhouse:** Schlafbaracke (*bunk:* Koje, Bett).
 rectangular: rechteckig.
7 **whitewashed:** (weiß) getüncht.
9 **latch:** (Tür-)Riegel, (Tür-)Griff.
11 f. **burlap ticking:** Inlett aus Sackleinen.
14 **occupant:** Inhaber.
16 **talcum powder:** (parfümierter) (Körper-)Puder.
 razors: Rasiermesser.
19 **vial:** Fläschchen, Gefäß.
20 **cast-iron:** Gußeisen.

ing. In the middle of the room stood a big square table littered with playing cards, and around it were grouped boxes for the players to sit on.

At about ten o'clock in the morning the sun threw a bright dust-laden bar through one of the side windows, and in and out of the beam flies shot like rushing stars.

The wooden latch raised. The door opened and a tall, stoop-shouldered old man came in. He was dressed in blue jeans and he carried a big push-broom in his left hand. Behind him came George, and behind George, Lennie.

"The boss was expectin' you last night," the old man said. "He was sore as hell when you wasn't here to go out this morning." He pointed with his right arm, and out of the sleeve came a round stick-like wrist, but no hand. "You can have them two beds there," he said, indicating two bunks near the stove.

George stepped over and threw his blankets down on the burlap sack of straw that was a mattress. He looked into his box shelf and then picked a small yellow can from it.

"Say. What the hell's this?"

"I don't know," said the old man.

"Says 'positively kills lice, roaches and other scourges.'

---

2 *(to be)* **littered with s.th.:** mit etwas (unordentlich) übersät sein.
5 **bar:** hier: Streifen, Strahl.
6 f. **rushing stars:** Sternschnuppen.
9 **stoop-shouldered:** mit hängenden Schultern.
10 **push-broom:** (Stiel-)Besen.
14 **sore as hell** (slang): stinksauer, wütend wie der Teufel.
25 **positively** (adv.): hier: garantiert.
   roach: Kurzform von *cockroach:* Küchenschabe, Kakerlake.
   scourge: hier: Ungeziefer.

What the hell kind of bed you giving us, anyways. We
don't want no pants rabbits."

The old swamper shifted his broom and held it between
his elbow and his side while he held out his hand for the
5 can. He studied the label carefully. "Tell you what –" he
said finally, "last guy that had this bed was a blacksmith
– hell of a nice fella and as clean a guy as you want to
meet. Used to wash his hands even *after* he ate."

"Then how come he got graybacks?" George was work-
10 ing up a slow anger. Lennie put his bindle on the
neighboring bunk and sat down. He watched George
with open mouth.

"Tell you what," said the old swamper. "This here
blacksmith – name of Whitey – was the kind of guy that
15 would put that stuff around even if there wasn't no bugs
– just to make sure, see? Tell you what he used to do –
At meals he'd peel his boil' potatoes, an' he'd take out
ever' little spot, no matter what kind, before he'd eat it.
And if there was a red splotch on an egg, he'd scrape it
20 off. Finally quit about the food. That's the kinda guy he
was – clean. Used ta dress up Sundays even when he
wasn't going no place, put on a necktie even, and then
set in the bunkhouse."

---

2 **pants rabbits** (slang): (Filz-)Läuse (*pants* [pl.]: Hose [AE]).
3 **swamper** (infml.): Mann für die Dreckarbeit (z. B. Saubermachen).
5 **label:** Etikett, Aufschrift.
7 **fella** (dial.): *fellow.*
9 **grayback** (slang): wörtl.: Graurücken; Laus.
14 **name of** (AE, infml.): mit Namen.
15 **bug:** Wanze.
19 **splotch:** Fleck, Klecks.
20 **to quit:** (infml.): (Stelle, Arbeit) aufgeben.
21 **ta** (dial.): *to.*

"I ain't so sure," said George skeptically. "What did you say he quit for?"

The old man put the yellow can in his pocket, and he rubbed his bristly white whiskers with his knuckles.
⁵ "Why ... he ... just quit, the way a guy will. Says it was the food. Just wanted to move. Didn't give no other reason but the food. Just says 'gimme my time' one night, the way any guy would."

George lifted his tick and looked underneath it. He
¹⁰ leaned over and inspected the sacking closely. Immediately Lennie got up and did the same with his bed. Finally George seemed satisfied. He unrolled his bindle and put things on the shelf, his razor and bar of soap, his comb and bottle of pills, his liniment and leather wrist-
¹⁵ band. Then he made his bed up neatly with blankets. The old man said, "I guess the boss'll be out here in a minute. He was sure burned when you wasn't here this morning. Come right in when we was eatin' breakfast and says, 'Where the hell's them new men?' An' he give
²⁰ the stable buck hell, too."

---

1 **skeptically** (adv.): skeptisch, zweifelnd.
4 **bristly** (auch: *bristled*): borstig, stoppelig.
   whiskers (pl.): Schnurrbart.
   knuckles (pl.): Fingerknöchel.
7 **gimme my time** (infml.): zahl mir meinen ausstehenden Lohn aus.
9 **tick:** Matratzenbezug.
10 **sacking:** Sackleinen.
14 **liniment:** Einreibemittel.
14 f. **wristband:** Armband.
17 **burned** (slang): verärgert, wütend, sauer.
19 f. **to give s.o. hell** (infml.): jdm. die Hölle heiß machen, jdn. schikanieren.
20 **stable buck** (AE): Stallknecht.

George patted a wrinkle out of his bed, and sat down.
"Give the stable buck hell?" he asked.

"Sure. Ya see the stable buck's a nigger."

"Nigger, huh?"

5 "Yeah. Nice fella too. Got a crooked back where a
horse kicked him. The boss gives him hell when he's
mad. But the stable buck don't give a damn about that.
He reads a lot. Got books in his room."

"What kind of a guy is the boss?" George asked.

10 "Well, he's a pretty nice fella. Gets pretty mad sometimes, but he's pretty nice. Tell ya what – know what he
done Christmas? Brang a gallon of whisky right in here
and says, 'Drink hearty, boys. Christmas comes but
once a year.'"

15 "The hell he did! Whole gallon?"

"Yes sir. Jesus, we had fun. They let the nigger come in
that night. Little skinner name of Smitty took after the
nigger. Done pretty good, too. The guys wouldn't let
him use his feet, so the nigger got him. If he coulda used
20 his feet, Smitty says he woulda killed the nigger. The
guys said on account of the nigger's got a crooked back,
Smitty can't use his feet." He paused in relish of the
memory. "After that the guys went into Soledad and

---

1 **wrinkle:** Falte.
5 **crooked:** krumm.
7 **mad** (AE, infml.): wütend.
12 **brang** (dial.): *brought.*
13 **hearty:** herzhaft.
17 **skinner** (slang): (Pferde- oder Maultier-)Gespannlenker.
   to take after s.o. (slang): hier: sich mit jdm. anlegen, mit jdm. eine
   Schlägerei anfangen.
19 **to get s.o.** (slang): jdn. verprügeln.
22 **relish:** Wohlgefallen, Genuß.

28

raised hell. I didn't go in there. I ain't got the poop no more."

Lennie was just finishing making his bed. The wooden latch raised again and the door opened. A little stocky man stood in the open doorway. He wore blue jean trousers, a flannel shirt, a black, unbuttoned vest and a black coat. His thumbs were stuck in his belt, on each side of a square steel buckle. On his head was a soiled brown Stetson hat, and he wore high-heeled boots and spurs to prove he was not a laboring man.

The old swamper looked quickly at him, and then shuffled to the door rubbing his whiskers with his knuckles as he went. "Them guys just come," he said, and shuffled past the boss and out the door.

The boss stepped into the room with the short, quick steps of a fat-legged man. "I wrote Murray and Ready I wanted two men this morning. You got your work slips?" George reached into his pocket and produced the slips and handed them to the boss. "It wasn't Murray and Ready's fault. Says right here on the slip that you was to be here for work this morning."

George looked down at his feet. "Bus driver give us a

---

1 **to raise hell** (slang): etwa: (die Stadt) auf den Kopf stellen.
   poop (slang): (fig.) Puste, Durchhaltevermögen, Mumm.
4 **stocky:** stämmig, gedrungen.
6 **flannel:** Flanell.
   vest: Weste (AE).
8 **buckle:** Schnalle.
9 **Stetson hat** (AE): Markenname für den vor allem in den Südstaaten sehr gebräuchlichen breitrandigen, hohen Filzhut.
12 **to shuffle:** schlurfen.
17 f. **work slip:** Vermittlungsnachweis.
22 f. **to give s.o. a bum steer** (slang): jdm. einen Bären aufbinden (*bum steer:* falsche Auskunft).

bum steer," he said. "We hadda walk ten miles. Says we was here when we wasn't. We couldn't get no rides in the morning."

The boss squinted his eyes. "Well, I had to send out the
5 grain teams short two buckers. Won't do any good to go out now till after dinner." He pulled his time book out of his pocket and opened it where a pencil was stuck between the leaves. George scowled meaningfully at Lennie, and Lennie nodded to show that he understood. The
10 boss licked his pencil. "What's your name?"

"George Milton."

"And what's yours?"

George said, "His name's Lennie Small."

The names were entered in the book. "Le's see, this is
15 the twentieth, noon the twentieth." He closed the book. "Where you boys been working?"

"Up around Weed," said George.

"You, too?" to Lennie.

"Yeah, him too," said George.

20 The boss pointed a playful finger at Lennie. "He ain't much of a talker, is he?"

"No, he ain't, but he's sure a hell of a good worker. Strong as a bull."

Lennie smiled to himself. "Strong as a bull," he repeat-
25 ed.

George scowled at him, and Lennie dropped his head in shame at having forgotten.

---

2 **to get a ride** (infml.): von jdm. (im Auto) mitgenommen werden.
4 **to squint one's eyes:** die Augen zusammenkneifen.
5 **grain team:** Erntehelferkolonne.
  short: mit ... zuwenig.
  bucker: Getreidepacker, jd., der Getreidesäcke auf- oder ablädt.
14 **le's** (dial.): *let's.*

The boss said suddenly, "Listen, Small!" Lennie raised his head. "What can you do?"

In a panic, Lennie looked at George for help. "He can do anything you tell him," said George. "He's a good
5 skinner. He can rassel grain bags, drive a cultivator. He can do anything. Just give him a try."

The boss turned on George. "Then why don't you let him answer? What you trying to put over?"

George broke in loudly, "Oh! I ain't saying he's bright.
10 He ain't. But I say he's a God damn good worker. He can put up a four hundred pound bale."

The boss deliberately put the little book in his pocket. He hooked his thumbs in his belt and squinted one eye nearly closed. "Say – what you sellin'?"
15 "Huh?"

"I said what stake you got in this guy? You takin' his pay away from him?"

"No, 'course I ain't. Why ya think I'm sellin' him out?"
20 "Well, I never seen one guy take so much trouble for another guy. I just like to know what your interest is."

George said, "He's my . . . cousin. I told his old lady I'd take care of him. He got kicked in the head by a horse when he was a kid. He's awright. Just ain't bright. But
25 he can do anything you tell him."

---

5 **to rassel** (slang): tragen, schleppen.
  cultivator: Kultivator, Grubber (Bodenbearbeitungsgerät).
11 **bale:** Ballen.
14 **What (are) you sellin'?** (slang): Was versuchst du mir aufzu-
   schwatzen?
16 **stake:** (finanzielles) Interesse, Anteil.
18 f. **to sell s.o. out** (slang): jdn. übers Ohr hauen, bescheißen.
22 **old lady** (infml.): Mutter, ,Alte'.

The boss turned half away. "Well, God knows he don't need any brains to buck barley bags. But don't you try to put nothing over, Milton. I got my eye on you. Why'd you quit in Weed?"

5 "Job was done," said George promptly.

"What kinda job?"

"We . . . we was diggin' a cesspool."

"All right. But don't try to put nothing over, 'cause you can't get away with nothing. I seen wise guys before. Go
10 on out with the grain teams after dinner. They're pickin' up barley at the threshing machine. Go out with Slim's team."

"Slim?"

"Yeah. Big tall skinner. You'll see him at dinner." He
15 turned abruptly and went to the door, but before he went out he turned and looked for a long moment at the two men.

When the sound of his footsteps had died away, George turned on Lennie. "So you wasn't gonna say a word.
20 You was gonna leave your big flapper shut and leave me do the talkin'. Damn near lost us the job."

Lennie stared hopelessly at his hands. "I forgot, George."

"Yeah, you forgot. You always forget, an' I got to talk
25 you out of it." He sat down heavily on the bunk. "Now he's got his eye on us. Now we got to be careful and not make no slips. You keep your big flapper shut after this." He fell morosely silent.

"George."

---

7 **cesspool:** Jauchegrube.
20 **flapper** (slang): ‚Klappe‘, Maul.
27 **slip:** (kleiner) Fehler.

"What you want now?"

"I wasn't kicked in the head with no horse, was I, George?"

"Be a damn good thing if you was," George said viciously. "Save ever'body a hell of a lot of trouble."

"You said I was your cousin, George."

"Well, that was a lie. An' I'm damn glad it was. If I was a relative of yours I'd shoot myself." He stopped suddenly, stepped to the open front door and peered out. "Say, what the hell you doin' listenin'?"

The old man came slowly into the room. He had his broom in his hand. At his heels there walked a drag-footed sheep dog, gray of muzzle, and with pale, blind old eyes. The dog struggled lamely to the side of the room and lay down, grunting softly to himself and licking his grizzled, moth-eaten coat. The swamper watched him until he was settled. "I wasn't listenin'. I was jus' standin' in the shade a minute scratchin' my dog. I jus' now finished swampin' out the wash house."

"You was pokin' your big ears into our business," George said. "I don't like nobody to get nosey."

The old man looked uneasily from George to Lennie, and then back. "I jus' come there," he said. "I didn't

---

4 f. **viciously** (adv.): bösartig.
12 f. **drag-footed:** hinkend.
13 **muzzle:** Maul.
15 **to grunt:** grunzen, brummen.
16 **grizzled** (infml.): ergraut.
   moth-eaten: von Motten zerfressen.
   coat: hier: Fell.
21 **to poke one's ears into s.o.'s business** (infml.): seine Nase in jds. Angelegenheiten stecken.
22 **nosey** (infml.): neugierig.

hear nothing you guys was sayin'. I ain't interested in nothing you was sayin'. A guy on a ranch don't never listen nor he don't ast no questions."

"Damn right he don't," said George, slightly mollified, "not if he wants to stay workin' long." But he was reassured by the swamper's defense. "Come on in and set down a minute," he said. "That's a hell of an old dog."

"Yeah. I had 'im ever since he was a pup. God, he was a good sheep dog when he was younger." He stood his broom against the wall and he rubbed his white bristled cheek with his knuckles. "How'd you like the boss?" he asked.

"Pretty good. Seemed awright."

"He's a nice fella," the swamper agreed. "You got to take him right."

At that moment a young man came into the bunkhouse; a thin young man with a brown face, with brown eyes and a head of tightly curled hair. He wore a work glove on his left hand, and, like the boss, he wore high-heeled boots. "Seen my old man?" he asked.

The swamper said, "He was here jus' a minute ago, Curley. Went over to the cook house, I think."

"I'll try to catch him," said Curley. His eyes passed over the new men and he stopped. He glanced coldly at George and then at Lennie. His arms gradually bent at the elbows and his hands closed into fists. He stiffened

---

3 **to ast** (dial.): *ask*.
4 **mollified:** beschwichtigt.
9 **'im** (auch *'um*; dial.): *him*.
16 **to take s.o. right** (infml.): jdn. zu nehmen wissen; jdn. richtig verstehen.
21 **old man** (infml.): Vater, ‚Alter'.

and went into a slight crouch. His glance was at once calculating and pugnacious. Lennie squirmed under the look and shifted his feet nervously. Curley stepped gingerly close to him. "You the new guys the old man was waitin' for?"

"We just come in," said George.

"Let the big guy talk."

Lennie twisted with embarrassment.

George said, "S'pose he don't want to talk?"

Curley lashed his body around. "By Christ, he's gotta talk when he's spoke to. What the hell are you gettin' into it for?"

"We travel together," said George coldly.

"Oh, so it's that way."

George was tense, and motionless. "Yeah, it's that way."

Lennie was looking helplessly to George for instruction.

"An' you won't let the big guy talk, is that it?"

"He can talk if he wants to tell you anything." He nodded slightly to Lennie.

"We jus' come in," said Lennie softly.

Curley stared levelly at him. "Well, nex' time you answer when you're spoke to." He turned toward the door and walked out, and his elbows were still bent out a little.

---

1 **to go into a crouch:** sich ducken.
2 **pugnacious:** kampflustig, streitsüchtig.
   to squirm: sich winden.
4 **gingerly** (adv.): vorsichtig, abstandend.
9 **s'pose** (dial.): *suppose.*
10 **to lash s.th. around:** etwas blitzschnell herumdrehen.
15 **tense:** gespannt.
23 **levelly** (adv.): ruhig, kühl.

George watched him out, and then he turned back to the swamper. "Say, what the hell's he got on his shoulder? Lennie didn't do nothing to him."

The old man looked cautiously at the door to make sure no one was listening. "That's the boss's son," he said quietly. "Curley's pretty handy. He done quite a bit in the ring. He's a lightweight, and he's handy."

"Well, let him be handy," said George. "He don't have to take after Lennie. Lennie didn't do nothing to him. What's he got against Lennie?"

The swamper considered. . . . "Well . . . tell you what. Curley's like a lot of little guys. He hates big guys. He's alla time picking scraps with big guys. Kind of like he's mad at 'em because he ain't a big guy. You seen little guys like that, ain't you? Always scrappy?"

"Sure," said George. "I seen plenty tough little guys. But this Curley better not make no mistakes about Lennie. Lennie ain't handy, but this Curley punk is gonna get hurt if he messes around with Lennie."

"Well, Curley's pretty handy," the swamper said skeptically. "Never did seem right to me. S'pose Curley jumps

---

2f. **What the hell's he got on his shoulder?** (infml.): Warum ist der so gereizt? (von *to have got a chip on one's shoulder*: sich ständig provoziert fühlen).

6 **to be handy** (infml.): hier: ein guter Boxer sein.

6f. **in the ring**: im Boxring.

7 **lightweight:** Leichtgewichtler (im Boxen Gewichtsklasse bis 61,23 kg).

13 **alla** (dial.): *all (of) the.*
   to pick scraps (slang): Raufereien, Schlägereien provozieren.

15 **scrappy** (AE, infml.): streitsüchtig.

16 **tough** (infml.): hart, handgreiflich.

18 **punk** (slang): drittklassiger Boxer; Rowdy.

19 **to mess around with s.o.** (slang): sich mit jdm. einlassen, anlegen.

21 **to jump s.o.** (slang): jdn. angreifen, auf jdn. losgehen.

a big guy an' licks him. Ever'body says what a game guy
Curley is. And s'pose he does the same thing and gets
licked. Then ever'body says the big guy oughtta pick
somebody his own size, and maybe they gang up on the
5 big guy. Never did seem right to me. Seems like Curley
ain't givin' nobody a chance."

George was watching the door. He said ominously,
"Well, he better watch out for Lennie. Lennie ain't no
fighter, but Lennie's strong and quick and Lennie don't
10 know no rules." He walked to the square table and sat
down on one of the boxes. He gathered some of the
cards together and shuffled them.

The old man sat down on another box. "Don't tell
Curley I said none of this. He'd slough me. He just
15 don't give a damn. Won't ever get canned 'cause his old
man's the boss."

George cut the cards and began turning them over,
looking at each one and throwing it down on a pile. He
said, "This guy Curley sounds like a son-of-a-bitch to
20 me. I don't like mean little guys."

"Seems to me like he's worse lately," said the swamper.
"He got married a couple of weeks ago. Wife lives over
in the boss's house. Seems like Curley is cockier'n ever
since he got married."

---

1 **to lick s.o.** (slang): jdn. verprügeln.
   game (infml.): mutig.
4 **to gang up on s.o.** (slang): sich gegen jdn. zusammentun, gemeinsam über jdn. herfallen.
7 **ominously** (adv.): unheilvoll.
12 **to shuffle:** (Karten) mischen.
14 **to slough s.o.** (slang): jdn. feuern, hinauswerfen.
15 **to get canned** (slang): gefeuert werden (*to can s.o.*: jdn. feuern).
17 **to cut:** (Karten) abheben.
23 **cockier'n** (dial.): *cockier than* (*cocky* [infml.]: großspurig).

George grunted, "Maybe he's showin' off for his wife."

The swamper warmed to his gossip. "You seen that glove on his left hand?"

5 "Yeah. I seen it."

"Well, that glove's fulla vaseline."

"Vaseline? What the hell for?"

"Well, I tell ya what – Curley says he's keepin' that hand soft for his wife."

10 George studied the cards absorbedly. "That's a dirty thing to tell around," he said.

The old man was reassured. He had drawn a derogatory statement from George. He felt safe now, and he spoke more confidently. "Wait'll you see Curley's wife."

15 George cut the cards again and put out a solitaire lay, slowly and deliberately. "Purty?" he asked casually."

"Yeah, Purty ... but —"

George studied his cards. "But what?"

20 "Well – she got the eye."

"Yeah? Married two weeks and got the eye? Maybe that's why Curley's pants is full of ants."

---

6 **vaseline:** Vaseline (Fettcreme).
12 **derogatory:** abwertend, geringschätzig.
14 **wait'll** (dial.): *wait till.*
15 **solitaire lay:** Kartenarrangement für eine Patience (*solitaire:* Patience [AE]).
16 **purty** (dial.): *pretty.*
16f. **casually** (adv.): beiläufig.
20 **to have got the eye** (slang): allen Männern schöne Augen machen.
22 **why Curley's pants is full of ants** (fig.): warum C. so kribbelig ist (*to have one's pants full of ants* [slang]: voller Unruhe sein).

"I seen her give Slim the eye. Slim's a jerkline skinner.
Hell of a nice fella. Slim don't need to wear no high-
heeled boots on a grain team. I seen her give Slim the
eye. Curley never seen it. An' I seen her give Carlson
5 the eye."

George pretended a lack of interest. "Looks like we was
gonna have fun."

The swamper stood up from his box. "Know what I
think?" George did not answer. "Well, I think Curley's
10 married ... a tart."

"He ain't the first," said George. "There's plenty done
that."

The old man moved toward the door, and his ancient
dog lifted his head and peered about, and then got
15 painfully to his feet to follow. "I gotta be settin' out the
wash basins for the guys. The teams'll be in before long.
You guys gonna buck barley?"

"Yeah."

"You won't tell Curley nothing I said?"

20 "Hell no."

"Well, you look her over, mister. You see if she ain't a
tart." He stepped out the door into the brilliant sunshine.

---

1 **to give s.o. the eye** (slang): jdm. schöne Augen machen, jdm. den
Kopf verdrehen.
jerkline: vor allem im Westen der USA gebräuchlicher, einzelner
Zügelriemen, der von der Bremse des Gespanns durch die Hand des
Lenkers direkt zur Kandare des Leitpferdes führt; *jerkline skinner*
ist hier im übertragenen Sinn zu verstehen als Bezeichnung
eines Mannes, der »die Zügel in der Hand hält«, d. h. absolute
Autorität genießt.
10 **tart** (slang): Nutte, Flittchen.
11 f. **there's plenty done that** (dial.): *there are plenty who have done
that.*

George laid down his cards thoughtfully, turned his piles of three. He built four clubs on his ace pile. The sun square was on the floor now, and the flies whipped through it like sparks. A sound of jingling harness and
5 the croak of heavy-laden axles sounded from outside. From the distance came a clear call. "Stable buck – ooh, sta-able buck!" And then, "Where the hell is that God damn nigger?"

George stared at his solitaire lay, and then he flounced
10 the cards together and turned around to Lennie. Lennie was lying down on the bunk watching him.

"Look, Lennie! This here ain't no setup. I'm scared. You gonna have trouble with that Curley guy. I seen that kind before. He was kinda feelin' you out. He
15 figures he's got you scared and he's gonna take a sock at you the first chance he gets."

Lennie's eyes were frightened. "I don't want no trouble," he said plaintively. "Don't let him sock me, George."

20 George got up and went over to Lennie's bunk and sat down on it. "I hate that kinda bastard," he said. "I seen plenty of 'em. Like the old guy says, Curley don't

---

2 **clubs** (pl.): Eichel, Kreuz (Spielkartenfarbe).
  ace: As.
3 **to whip:** hier: schwirren.
4 **to jingle:** klirren, klimpern, rasseln.
  harness: Pferdegeschirr.
5 **croak:** Krächzen, Ächzen.
  axle: Achse.
9 **to flounce s.th together:** etwas ärgerlich zusammenwerfen.
12 **setup** (slang): leichte Aufgabe, Spielerei, (fig.) Spaziergang.
14 **to feel s.o. out** (slang): jdn. abtasten, jdm. auf den Zahn fühlen.
15f. **to take a sock at s.o.** (slang): jdm. eine verpassen.
18 **plaintively** (adv.): kläglich.

take no chances. He always wins." He thought for a moment. "If he tangles with you, Lennie, we're gonna get the can. Don't make no mistake about that. He's the boss's son. Look, Lennie. You try to keep away from him, will you? Don't never speak to him. If he comes in here you move clear to the other side of the room. Will you do that, Lennie?"

"I don't want no trouble," Lennie mourned. "I never done nothing to him."

"Well, that won't do you no good if Curley wants to plug himself up for a fighter. Just don't have nothing to do with him. Will you remember?"

"Sure, George. I ain't gonna say a word."

The sound of the approaching grain teams was louder, thud of big hooves on hard ground, drag of brakes and the jingle of trace chains. Men were calling back and forth from the teams. George, sitting on the bunk beside Lennie, frowned as he thought. Lennie asked timidly, "You ain't mad, George?"

"I ain't mad at you. I'm mad at this here Curley bastard. I hoped we was gonna get a little stake together – maybe a hundred dollars." His tone grew decisive. "You keep away from Curley, Lennie."

"Sure I will, George. I won't say a word."

"Don't let him pull you in – but – if the son-of-a-bitch socks you – let 'im have it."

---

1 **to take no chances** (infml.): keine Risiken eingehen.
2 **to tangle with s.o.** (infml.): sich mit jdm. prügeln.
3 **to get the can** (slang): seine Papiere bekommen, gefeuert werden.
11 **to plug o.s. up for s.th.** (infml.): etwas an sich herauskehren, sich als etwas aufspielen.
15 **thud:** dumpfer Schlag, schwerer Tritt.
hooves: Hufe.
16 **trace chain:** Kette am Zugriemen (bei Pferdegespannen).

"Let 'im have what, George?"

"Never mind, never mind. I'll tell you when. I hate that kind of a guy. Look, Lennie, if you get in any kind of trouble, you remember what I told you to do?"

5 Lennie raised up on his elbow. His face contorted with thought. Then his eyes moved sadly to George's face. "If I get in any trouble, you ain't gonna let me tend the rabbits."

"That's not what I meant. You remember where we
10 slep' last night? Down by the river?"

"Yeah. I remember. Oh, sure I remember! I go there an' hide in the brush."

"Hide till I come for you. Don't let nobody see you. Hide in the brush by the river. Say that over."

15 "Hide in the brush by the river, down in the brush by the river."

"If you get in trouble."

"If I get in trouble."

A brake screeched outside. A call came, "Stable – buck.
20 Oh! Sta-able buck."

George said, "Say it over to yourself, Lennie, so you won't forget it."

Both men glanced up, for the rectangle of sunshine in the doorway was cut off. A girl was standing there
25 looking in. She had full, rouged lips and wide-spaced eyes, heavily made up. Her fingernails were red. Her hair hung in little rolled clusters, like sausages. She

---

5 **to contort:** sich verzerren.
14 **to say s.th. over:** etwas wiederholen, wiederholt vor sich hin sagen.
19 **to screech:** kreischen, schreien.
23 **rectangle:** Rechteck.
25 **rouged:** rot angemalt.
26 **made up:** bemalt, geschminkt.

wore a cotton house dress and red mules, on the insteps
of which were little bouquets of red ostrich feathers.
"I'm lookin' for Curley," she said. Her voice had a
nasal, brittle quality.

5 George looked away from her and then back. "He was
in here a minute ago, but he went."

"Oh!" She put her hands behind her back and leaned
against the door frame so that her body was thrown
forward. "You're the new fellas that just come, ain't
10 ya?"

"Yeah."

Lennie's eyes moved down over her body, and though
she did not seem to be looking at Lennie she bridled a
little. She looked at her fingernails. "Sometimes Cur-
15 ley's in here," she explained.

George said brusquely, "Well he ain't now."

"If he ain't, I guess I better look some place else," she
said playfully.

Lennie watched her, fascinated. George said, "If I see
20 him, I'll pass the word you was looking for him."

She smiled archly and twitched her body. "Nobody
can't blame a person for lookin'," she said. There were
footsteps behind her, going by. She turned her head.

---

1 **house dress** (AE): Schürzenkleid.
  mule (dial.): absatzloser Pantoffel.
  instep: Spann, Rist.
2 **bouquet:** (Blumen-)Strauß.
  ostrich: Strauß (Vogelart).
4 **nasal:** nasal, näselnd.
  brittle: spröde.
13 **to bridle:** den Kopf zurückwerfen.
20 **to pass the word** (infml.): etwas weitersagen, ausrichten.
21 **archly** (adv.): schelmisch, durchtrieben.
  to twitch one's body: mit den Hüften wippen.

"Hi, Slim," she said.

Slim's voice came through the door. "Hi, Good-lookin'."

"I'm tryin' to find Curley, Slim."

5 "Well, you ain't tryin' very hard. I seen him goin' in your house."

She was suddenly apprehensive. "'Bye, boys," she called into the bunkhouse, and she hurried away.

George looked around at Lennie. "Jesus, what a 10 tramp," he said. "So that's what Curley picks for a wife."

"She's purty," said Lennie defensively.

"Yeah, and she's sure hidin' it. Curley got his work ahead of him. Bet she'd clear out for twenty 15 bucks."

Lennie still stared at the doorway where she had been. "Gosh, she was purty." He smiled admiringly. George looked quickly down at him and then he took him by an ear and shook him.

20 "Listen to me, you crazy bastard," he said fiercely. "Don't you even take a look at that bitch. I don't care what she says and what she does. I seen 'em poison before, but I never seen no piece of jail bait worse than her. You leave her be."

---

7 **apprehensive:** furchtsam, besorgt.

10 **tramp** (slang): mannstolles Weib.

14 **to clear out** (AE, infml.): sich aus dem Staub machen; hier: den Ehepartner sitzenlassen.

17 **gosh** (infml.): Mensch!

22 **'em poison** (slang): *that kind of poison:* die Art von Unglücks-bringer.

23 **jail bait** (slang): etwa: Sorte Mädchen, die einen Mann ins Gefängnis bringen kann.

24 **to leave s.o. be** (dial.): jdn. in Ruhe lassen.

Lennie tried to disengage his ear. "I never done nothing, George."

"No, you never. But when she was standin' in the doorway showin' her legs, you wasn't lookin' the other way, neither."

"I never meant no harm, George. Honest I never."

"Well, you keep away from her, 'cause she's a rattrap if I ever seen one. You let Curley take the rap. He let himself in for it. Glove fulla vaseline," George said disgustedly. "An' I bet he's eatin' raw eggs and writin' to the patent medicine houses."

Lennie cried out suddenly – "I don't like this place, George. This ain't no good place. I wanna get outa here."

"We gotta keep it till we get a stake. We can't help it, Lennie. We'll get out jus' as soon as we can. I don't like it no better than you do." He went back to the table and set out a new solitaire hand. "No, I don't like it," he said. "For two bits I'd shove out of here. If we can get jus' a few dollars in the poke we'll shove off and go up the American River and pan gold. We can make maybe

---

8 **to take the rap** (slang): den schwarzen Peter haben, (mit etwas) angeschmiert sein, (etwas) ausbaden.

8f. **to let o.s. in for s.th.** (infml.): sich etwas aufhalsen, sich eine Suppe mit etwas einbrocken.

11 **patent medicine house** (AE): Versand für patentrechtlich geschützte Arzneimittel (gemeint sind in erster Linie sexuelle Stimulantien).

18 **hand:** Blatt, Karten.

19 **for two bits** (slang): für einen Vierteldollar, für 25 Cent; (fig.) für einen Appel und ein Ei.

to shove out (slang): abhauen.

20 **poke** (slang): Tasche; Börse.

21 **American River:** Fluß nordöstlich von Sacramento (Ausgangspunkt des kalifornischen Goldrausches im Jahre 1848).

to pan gold (infml.): Gold waschen (in einer pfannenförmigen Schüssel).

a couple of dollars a day there, and we might hit a pocket."

Lennie leaned eagerly toward him. "Le's go, George. Le's get outa here. It's mean here."

5 "We gotta stay," George said shortly. "Shut up now. The guys'll be comin' in."

From the washroom nearby came the sound of running water and rattling basins. George studied the cards. "Maybe we oughtta wash up," he said. "But we ain't

10 done nothing to get dirty."

A tall man stood in the doorway. He held a crushed Stetson hat under his arm while he combed his long, black, damp hair straight back. Like the others he wore blue jeans and a short denim jacket. When he had

15 finished combing his hair he moved into the room, and he moved with a majesty achieved only by royalty and master craftsmen. He was a jerkline skinner, the prince of the ranch, capable of driving ten, sixteen, even twenty mules with a single line to the leaders. He was

20 capable of killing a fly on the wheeler's butt with a bull whip without touching the mule. There was a gravity in his manner and a quiet so profound that all talk stopped when he spoke. His authority was so great that his word was taken on any subject, be it politics or love. This was

25 Slim, the jerkline skinner. His hatchet face was ageless. He might have been thirty-five or fifty. His ear heard more than was said to him, and his slow speech had

---

1 f. **to hit a pocket** (infml.): auf eine Goldader stoßen.
19 **with a single line to the leaders:** mit nur einem Zügel zu den Leitmaultieren.
20 **wheeler's butt** (slang): Flanke des hintersten Zugtieres.
22 **profound:** tief(gründig).
25 **hatchet face** (fig.): scharfgeschnittenes Gesicht (*hatchet:* Beil).

46

overtones not of thought, but of understanding beyond thought. His hands, large and lean, were as delicate in their action as those of a temple dancer.

He smoothed out his crushed hat, creased it in the
5 middle and put it on. He looked kindly at the two in the bunkhouse. "It's brighter'n a bitch outside," he said gently. "Can't hardly see nothing in here. You the new guys?"

"Just come", said George.

10 "Gonna buck barley?"

"That's what the boss says."

Slim sat down on a box across the table from George. He studied the solitaire hand that was upside down to him. "Hope you get on my team," he said. His voice
15 was very gentle. "I gotta pair of punks on my team that don't know a barley bag from a blue ball. You guys ever bucked any barley?"

"Hell, yes," said George. "I ain't nothing to scream about, but that big bastard there can put up more grain
20 alone than most pairs can."

Lennie, who had been following the conversation back and forth with his eyes, smiled complacently at the compliment. Slim looked approvingly at George for having given the compliment. He leaned over the table

---

1 **overtones** (fig.): Untertöne.
2 **lean:** hager.
4 **to crease:** kniffen.
16 **not to know a barley bag from a blue ball** (slang): wörtl.: einen (aus blauem Tuch gefertigten) Gerstensack nicht von einem blauen Ball unterscheiden können; (fig.) keine Ahnung von der Arbeit haben.
18 f. **nothing to scream about** (infml.): nichts Besonderes, nicht überwältigend.
22 **complacently** (adv.): selbstzufrieden.

and snapped the corner of a loose card. "You guys travel around together?" His tone was friendly. It invited confidence without demanding it.

"Sure," said George. "We kinda look after each other."
5 He indicated Lennie with his thumb. "He ain't bright. Hell of a good worker, though. Hell of a nice fella, but he ain't bright. I've knew him for a long time."

Slim looked through George and beyond him. "Ain't many guys travel around together," he mused. "I don't
10 know why. Maybe ever'body in the whole damn world is scared of each other."

"It's a lot nicer to go around with a guy you know," said George.

A powerful, big-stomached man came into the bunk-
15 house. His head still dripped water from the scrubbing and dousing. "Hi, Slim," he said, and then stopped and stared at George and Lennie.

"These guys jus' come," said Slim by way of introduction.

20 "Glad ta meet ya," the big man said. "My name's Carlson."

"I'm George Milton. This here's Lennie Small."

"Glad ta meet ya," Carlson said again. "He ain't very small." He chuckled softly at his joke. "Ain't small at
25 all," he repeated. "Meant to ask you, Slim – how's your bitch? I seen she wasn't under your wagon this morning."

---

8 f. **ain't many guys** (dial.): *there aren't many guys who.*
15 **to scrub:** sich schrubben.
16 **to douse:** sich mit Wasser übergießen.
18 **by way of:** als.
24 **to chuckle:** kichern, glucksen.
26 **bitch:** Hündin.

"She slang her pups last night," said Slim. "Nine of 'em. I drowned four of 'em right off. She couldn't feed that many."

"Got five left, huh?"

5 "Yeah, five. I kept the biggest."

"What kinda dogs you think they're gonna be?"

"I dunno," said Slim. "Some kinda shepherds, I guess. That's the most kind I seen around here when she was in heat."

10 Carlson went on, "Got five pups, huh. Gonna keep all of 'em?"

"I dunno. Have to keep 'em a while so they can drink Lulu's milk."

Carlson said thoughtfully, "Well, looka here, Slim. I 15 been thinkin'. That dog of Candy's is so God damn old he can't hardly walk. Stinks like hell, too. Ever' time he comes into the bunkhouse I can smell him for two, three days. Why'n't you get Candy to shoot his old dog and give him one of the pups to raise up? I can smell that 20 dog a mile away. Got no teeth, damn near blind, can't eat. Candy feeds him milk. He can't chew nothing else."

George had been staring intently at Slim. Suddenly a triangle began to ring outside, slowly at first, and then 25 faster and faster until the beat of it disappeared into one ringing sound. It stopped as suddenly as it had started.

---

1 **to sling:** (Welpen) werfen.
7 **I dunno** (dial.): *I don't know.*
  shepherd: Schäferhund.
8f. **in heat:** läufig.
14 **looka** (dial.): *look.*
24 **triangle:** Triangel (Schlaginstrument).

"There she goes," said Carlson.

Outside, there was a burst of voices as a group of men went by.

Slim stood up slowly and with dignity. "You guys better
5 come on while they's still something to eat. Won't be nothing left in a couple of minutes."

Carlson stepped back to let Slim precede him, and then the two of them went out the door.

Lennie was watching George excitedly. George rum-
10 pled his cards into a messy pile. "Yeah!" George said, "I heard him, Lennie. I'll ask him."

"A brown and white one," Lennie cried excitedly.

"Come on. Le's get dinner. I don't know whether he got a brown and white one."

15 Lennie didn't move from his bunk. "You ask him right away, George, so he won't kill no more of 'em."

"Sure. Come on now, get up on your feet."

Lennie rolled off his bunk and stood up, and the two of them started for the door. Just as they reached it,
20 Curley bounced in.

"You seen a girl around here?" he demanded angrily.

George said coldly, "'Bout half an hour ago maybe."

25 "Well what the hell was she doin'?"

George stood still, watching the angry little man. He said insultingly, "She said – she was lookin' for you."

---

9 f. **to rumple:** achtlos wurschteln.
10 **messy pile:** ungeordneter Haufen, Durcheinander.
20 **to bounce in** (infml.): hereinplatzen.

Curley seemed really to see George for the first time. His eyes flashed over George, took in his height, measured his reach, looked at his trim middle. "Well, which way'd she go?" he demanded at last.

5 "I dunno," said George. "I didn't watch her go."

Curley scowled at him, and turning, hurried out the door.

George said, "Ya know, Lennie, I'm scared I'm gonna tangle with that bastard myself. I hate his guts. Jesus
10 Christ! Come on. They won't be a damn thing left to eat."

They went out the door. The sunshine lay in a thin line under the window. From a distance there could be heard a rattle of dishes.

15 After a moment the ancient dog walked lamely in through the open door. He gazed about with mild, half-blind eyes. He sniffed, and then lay down and put his head between his paws. Curley popped into the door-way again and stood looking into the room. The dog
20 raised his head, but when Curley jerked out, the grizzled head sank to the floor again.

Three

Although there was evening brightness showing through the windows of the bunkhouse, inside it was dusk.
25 Through the open door came the thuds and occasional

---

3 **trim middle:** schlanke Taille.
9 **to hate s.o.'s guts** (infml.): jdn. abgrundtief hassen, auf den Tod nicht ausstehen können.
18 **to pop into s.th.** (infml.): schnell mal in etwas ‚hereinschauen'.

clangs of a horseshoe game, and now and then the
sound of voices raised in approval or derision.
Slim and George came into the darkening bunkhouse
together. Slim reached up over the card table and
5 turned on the tin-shaded electric light. Instantly the
table was brilliant with light, and the cone of the shade
threw its brightness straight downward, leaving the
corners of the bunkhouse still in dusk. Slim sat down on
a box and George took his place opposite.
10 "It wasn't nothing," said Slim. "I would of had to
drowned most of 'em anyways. No need to thank me
about that."
George said, "It wasn't much to you, maybe, but it was
a hell of a lot to him. Jesus Christ, I don't know how
15 we're gonna get him to sleep in here. He'll want to sleep
right out in the barn with 'em. We'll have trouble
keepin' him from getting right in the box with them
pups."
"It wasn't nothing," Slim repeated. "Say, you sure was
20 right about him. Maybe he ain't bright, but I never seen
such a worker. He damn near killed his partner buckin'
barley. There ain't nobody can keep up with him. God
awmighty, I never seen such a strong guy."
George spoke proudly. "Jus' tell Lennie what to do an'
25 he'll do it if it don't take no figuring. He can't think of
nothing to do himself, but he sure can take orders."

---

1 **clang:** Klirren.
 horseshoe game: Hufeisenwerfen (Spiel, mit dem auf eine verein-
 barte Entfernung ein Hufeisen um eine in den Boden geschlagene
 [Metall-]Stange geworfen werden muß).
2 **derision:** Spott.
5 **tin-shaded:** mit einem Blechschirm.
6 **cone:** Kegel.
25 **to take:** erfordern.

There was a clang of horseshoe on iron stake outside
and a little cheer of voices.

Slim moved back slightly so the light was not on his
face. "Funny how you an' him string along together." It
was Slim's calm invitation to confidence.

"What's funny about it?" George demanded defensively.

"Oh, I dunno. Hardly none of the guys ever travel
together. I hardly never seen two guys travel together.
You know how the hands are, they just come in and get
their bunk and work a month, and then they quit and go
out alone. Never seem to give a damn about nobody. It
jus' seems kinda funny a cuckoo like him and a smart
little guy like you travelin' together."

"He ain't no cuckoo," said George. "He's dumb as hell,
but he ain't crazy. An' I ain't so bright neither, or I
wouldn't be buckin' barley for my fifty and found. If I
was bright, if I was even a little bit smart, I'd have my
own little place, an' I'd be bringin' in my own crops,
'stead of doin' all the work and not getting what comes
up outa the ground." George fell silent. He wanted to
talk. Slim neither encouraged nor discouraged him. He
just sat back quiet and receptive.

"It ain't so funny, him an' me goin' aroun' together,"
George said at last. "Him and me was both born in

---

4 **to string along together** (slang): einander folgen, hintereinanderher-
laufen.
10 **hand:** *farm hand:* Farmarbeiter.
13 **cuckoo** (slang): Idiot, Geisteskranker.
15 **dumb** (AE, infml.): blöd, doof.
17 **fifty and found** (AE, infml.): fünfzig Dollar plus Kost und Logis.
20 **'stead** (dial.): *instead.*
23 **receptive:** empfänglich, aufnahmebereit.

Auburn. I knowed his Aunt Clara. She took him when he was a baby and raised him up. When his Aunt Clara died, Lennie just come along with me out workin'. Got kinda used to each other after a little while."

5 "Umm," said Slim.

George looked over at Slim and saw the calm, Godlike eyes fastened on him. "Funny," said George. "I used to have a hell of a lot of fun with 'im. Used to play jokes on 'im 'cause he was too dumb to take care of 'imself. But he was too dumb even to know he had a joke played on him. I had fun. Made me seem God damn smart alongside of him. Why he'd do any damn thing I tol' him. If I tol' him to walk over a cliff, over he'd go. That wasn't so damn much fun after a while. He never got mad about it, neither. I've beat the hell outa him, and he coulda bust every bone in my body jus' with his han's, but he never lifted a finger against me." George's voice was taking on the tone of confession. "Tell you what made me stop that. One day a bunch of guys was standin' around up on the Sacramento River. I was feelin' pretty smart. I turns to Lennie and says, 'Jump in.' An' he jumps. Couldn't swim a stroke. He damn near drowned before we could get him. An' he was so damn nice to me for pullin' him out. Clean forgot I told him to jump in. Well, I ain't done nothing like that no more."

---

1 **Auburn:** Stadt in Kalifornien, etwa 50 km nordöstlich von Sacramento.
11 f. **alongside of:** hier: verglichen mit.
16 **to bust** (slang): (zer)brechen.
19 **bunch** (infml.): Gruppe, Clique.
22 **stroke:** Armzug (beim Schwimmen).
24 **clean** (adv.): völlig.

54

"He's a nice fella," said Slim. "Guy don't need no sense to be a nice fella. Seems to me sometimes it jus' works the other way around. Take a real smart guy and he ain't hardly ever a nice fella."

George stacked the scattered cards and began to lay out his solitaire hand. The shoes thudded on the ground outside. At the windows the light of the evening still made the window squares bright.

"I ain't got no people," George said. "I seen the guys that go around on the ranches alone. That ain't no good. They don't have no fun. After a long time they get mean. They get wantin' to fight all the time."

"Yeah, they get mean," Slim agreed. "They get so they don't want to talk to nobody."

"'Course Lennie's a God damn nuisance most of the time," said George. "But you get used to goin' around with a guy an' you can't get rid of him."

"He ain't mean," said Slim. "I can see Lennie ain't a bit mean."

"'Course he ain't mean. But he gets in trouble alla time because he's so God damn dumb. Like what happened in Weed —" He stopped, stopped in the middle of turning over a card. He looked alarmed and peered over at Slim. "You wouldn't tell nobody?"

"What'd he do in Weed?" Slim asked calmly.

"You wouldn't tell? ... No, 'course you wouldn'."

"What'd he do in Weed?" Slim asked again.

"Well, he seen this girl in a red dress. Dumb bastard

---

5 **to stack:** stapeln.
6 **to thud:** dumpf aufschlagen, dröhnen.
15 **nuisance:** Ärgernis.

like he is, he wants to touch ever'thing he likes. Just
wants to feel it. So he reaches out to feel this red dress
an' the girl lets out a squawk, and that gets Lennie all
mixed up, and he holds on 'cause that's the only thing
he can think to do. Well, this girl squawks and squawks.
I was jus' a little bit off, and I heard all the yellin', so I
comes running, an' by that time Lennie's so scared all
he can think to do is jus' hold on. I socked him over the
head with a fence picket to make him let go. He was so
scairt he couldn't let go of that dress. And he's so God
damn strong, you know."
Slim's eyes were level and unwinking. He nodded very
slowly. "So what happens?"
George carefully built his line of solitaire cards. "Well,
that girl rabbits in an' tells the law she been raped. The
guys in Weed start a party out to lynch Lennie. So we sit
in a irrigation ditch under water all the rest of that day.
Got on'y our heads sticking outa water, an' up under
the grass that sticks out from the side of the ditch. An'
that night we scrammed outa there."
Slim sat in silence for a moment. "Didn't hurt the girl
none, huh?" he asked finally.

    3 **squawk:** heiserer Schrei.
    4 **mixed up:** verwirrt, durcheinander.
    9 **fence picket:** Zaunpfahl.
   10 **scairt** (dial.): *scared.*
   12 **unwinking:** starr (*to wink:* blinzeln).
   15 **to rabbit in** (slang): etwa: reinlaufen und drauflosplappern (von
      rabbit and pork [rhyming slang]: *talk*).
      to rape: vergewaltigen.
   16 **party:** (Verfolgungs-)Trupp.
      to lynch: lynchen, ohne Gerichtsverhandlung aufhängen.
   18 **on'y** (dial.): *only.*
   20 **to scram** (slang): Fersengeld geben, verduften.

"Hell, no. He just scared her. I'd be scared too if he grabbed me. But he never hurt her. He jus' wanted to touch that red dress, like he wants to pet them pups all the time.."

"He ain't mean," said Slim. "I can tell a mean guy a mile off."

"'Course he ain't, and he'll do any damn thing I —"

Lennie came in through the door. He wore his blue denim coat over his shoulders like a cape, and he walked hunched way over.

"Hi, Lennie," said George. "How you like the pup now?"

Lennie said breathlessly, "He's brown an' white jus' like I wanted." He went directly to his bunk and lay down and turned his face to the wall and drew up his knees.

George put down his cards very deliberately. "Lennie," he said sharply.

Lennie twisted his neck and looked over his shoulder.

"Huh? What you want, George?"

"I tol' you you couldn't bring that pup in here."

"What pup, George? I ain't got no pup."

George went quickly to him, grabbed him by the shoulder and rolled him over. He reached down and picked the tiny puppy from where Lennie had been concealing it against his stomack.

Lennie sat up quickly. "Give 'um to me, George."

George said, "You get right up an' take this pup back to the nest. He's gotta sleep with his mother. You want to

---

2 **to grab:** packen.
10 **hunched way over** (AE, infml.): weit vornübergebeugt (*hunch*: Buckel).

kill him? Just born last night an' you take him out of the nest. You take him back or I'll tell Slim not to let you have him."

Lennie held out his hands pleadingly. "Give 'um to me,
5 George. I'll take 'um back. I didn't mean no harm, George. Honest I didn't. I jus' wanted to pet 'um a little."

George handed the pup to him. "Awright. You get him back there quick, and don't you take him out no more.
10 You'll kill him, the first thing you know." Lennie fairly scuttled out of the room.

Slim had not moved. His calm eyes followed Lennie out the door. "Jesus," he said. "He's jus' like a kid, ain't he?"

15 "Sure he's jes' like a kid. There ain't no more harm in him than a kid neither, except he's so strong. I bet he won't come in here to sleep tonight. He'd sleep right alongside that box in the barn. Well – let 'im. He ain't doin' no harm out there."

20 It was almost dark outside now. Old Candy, the swamper, came in and went to his bunk, and behind him struggled his old dog. "Hello, Slim. Hello, George. Didn't neither of you play horseshoes?"

"I don't like to play ever' night," said Slim.

25 Candy went on, "Either you guys got a slug of whisky? I gotta gut ache."

"I ain't," said Slim. "I'd drink it myself if I had, an' I ain't got a gut ache neither."

---

10 **fairly** (adv.): hier: als ob der Teufel hinter ihm her wäre.
11 **to scuttle:** sich davonmachen, flitzen.
25 **slug:** Schluck.
26 **gut ache:** Bauchschmerzen.

"Gotta bad gut ache," said Candy. "Them God damn turnips give it to me. I knowed they was going to before I ever eat 'em."

The thick-bodied Carlson came in out of the darkening

5 yard. He walked to the other end of the bunkhouse and turned on the second shaded light. "Darker'n hell in here," he said. "Jesus, how that nigger can pitch shoes."

"He's plenty good," said Slim.

10 "Damn right he is," said Carlson. "He don't give nobody else a chance to win —" He stopped and sniffed the air, and still sniffing, looked down at the old dog. "God awmighty, that dog stinks. Get him outa here, Candy! I don't know nothing that stinks as bad as an old

15 dog. You gotta get him out."

Candy rolled to the edge of his bunk. He reached over and patted the ancient dog, and he apologized, "I been around him so much I never notice how he stinks."

"Well, I can't stand him in here," said Carlson. "That

20 stink hangs around even after he's gone." He walked over with his heavy-legged stride and looked down at the dog. "Got no teeth," he said. "He's all stiff with rheumatism. He ain't no good to you, Candy. An' he ain't no good to himself. Why'n't you shoot him,

25 Candy?"

The old man squirmed uncomfortably. "Well – hell! I had him so long. Had him since he was a pup. I herded sheep with him." He said proudly, "You wouldn't think

---

2 **turnip:** (Steck-)Rübe.

7 f. **to pitch shoes** (slang): Hufeisen werfen.

9 **plenty** (dial.): *very*.

it to look at him now, but he was the best damn sheep
dog I ever seen."

George said, "I seen a guy in Weed that had an
Airedale could herd sheep. Learned it from the other
5 dogs."

Carlson was not to be put off. "Look, Candy. This ol'
dog jus' suffers hisself all the time. If you was to take
him out and shoot him right in the back of the head –"
he leaned over and pointed, "– right there, why he'd
10 never know what hit him."

Candy looked about unhappily. "No," he said softly.
"No, I couldn't do that. I had 'im too long."

"He don't have no fun," Carlson insisted. "And he stinks
to beat hell. Tell you what. I'll shoot him for you. Then
15 it won't be you that does it."

Candy threw his legs off his bunk. He scratched the
white stubble whiskers on his cheek nervously. "I'm
so used to him," he said softly. "I had him from a
pup."

20 "Well, you ain't bein' kind to him keepin' him alive,"
said Carlson. "Look, Slim's bitch got a litter right now. I
bet Slim would give you one of them pups to raise up,
wouldn't you, Slim?"

The skinner had been studying the old dog with his calm
25 eyes. "Yeah," he said. "You can have a pup if you want
to." He seemed to shake himself free for speech. "Carl's
right, Candy. That dog ain't no good to himself. I wisht
somebody'd shoot me if I get old an' a cripple."

---

4 **Airedale:** Hunderasse (Terrierart).
7 **to suffer o.s.** (infml.): sich abquälen, dahinvegetieren.
  hisself (dial.): *himself.*
17 **stubble:** Stoppeln, Stoppel-.
21 **litter:** Wurf (Jungtiere).

Candy looked helplessly at him, for Slim's opinions were law. "Maybe it'd hurt him," he suggested. "I don't mind takin' care of him."

Carlson said, "The way I'd shoot him, he wouldn't feel
5 nothing. I'd put the gun right there." He pointed with his toe. "Right back of the head. He wouldn't even quiver."

Candy looked for help from face to face. It was quite dark outside by now. A young laboring man came in.
10 His sloping shoulders were bent forward and he walked heavily on his heels, as though he carried the invisible grain bag. He went to his bunk and put his hat on his shelf. Then he picked a pulp magazine from his shelf and brought it to the light over the table. "Did I show
15 you this, Slim?" he asked.

"Show me what?"

The young man turned to the back of the magazine, put it down on the table and pointed with his finger. "Right there, read that." Slim bent over it. "Go on," said the
20 young man. "Read it out loud."

"'Dear Editor,'" Slim read slowly. "'I read your mag for six years and I think it is the best on the market. I like stories by Peter Rand. I think he is a whing-ding. Give us more like the Dark Rider. I don't write many letters.
25 Just thought I would tell you I think your mag is the best dime's worth I ever spent.'"

Slim looked up questioningly. "What you want me to read that for?"

13 **pulp magazine** (AE): Schundillustrierte (hergestellt aus billigem, rauhem, holzreichem Papier) (*wood pulp:* Holzschliff).
21 **mag** (slang): Kurzform von *magazine*.
23 **Rand:** Peter R., Schreiber von trivialen Westernstories.
   a whing-ding (slang): eine Wucht, ein Heuler.
25 f. **the best dime's worth:** die am besten angelegten 10 Cent.

Whit said, "Go on. Read the name at the bottom."
Slim read, "'Yours for success, William Tenner.'" He
glanced up at Whit again. "What you want me to read
that for?"

5 Whit closed the magazine impressively. "Don't you
remember Bill Tenner? Worked here about three
months ago?"
Slim thought. ... "Little guy?" he asked. "Drove a
cultivator?"

10 "That's him," Whit cried. "That's the guy!"
"You think he's the guy wrote this letter?"
"I know it. Bill and me was in here one day. Bill had
one of them books that just come. He was lookin' in it
and he says, 'I wrote a letter. Wonder if they put it in
15 the book!' But it wasn't there. Bill says, 'Maybe they're
savin' it for later.' An' that's just what they done. There
it is."
"Guess you're right," said Slim. "Got it right in the
book."

20 George held out his hand for the magazine. "Let's look
at it?"
Whit found the place again, but he did not surrender his
hold on it. He pointed out the letter with his forefinger.
And then he went to his box shelf and laid the magazine
25 carefully in. "I wonder if Bill seen it," he said. "Bill and
me worked in that patch of field peas. Run cultivators,
both of us. Bill was a hell of a nice fella."
During the conversation Carlson had refused to be

---

22 **to surrender:** hier: lockern.
26 **field peas** (pl.): Erbsenart, die in den USA im großen Stil als
Futterpflanze angebaut wird.

drawn in. He continued to look down at the old dog.
Candy watched him uneasily. At last Carlson said, "If
you want me to, I'll put the old devil out of his misery
right now and get it over with. Ain't nothing left for
5 him. Can't eat, can't see, can't even walk without
hurtin'.."
Candy said hopefully, "You ain't got no gun."
"The hell I ain't. Got a Luger. It won't hurt him none at
all."
10 Candy said, "Maybe tomorra. Le's wait till tomorra."
"I don't see no reason for it," said Carlson. He went to
his bunk, pulled his bag from underneath it and took
out a Luger pistol. "Le's get it over with," he said. "We
15 can't sleep with him stinkin' around in here." He put the
pistol in his hip pocket.
Candy looked a long time at Slim to try to find some
reversal. And Slim gave him none. At last Candy said
softly and hopelessly, "Awright – take 'im." He did not
20 look down at the dog at all. He lay back on his bunk and
crossed his arms behind his head and stared at the
ceiling.
From his pocket Carlson took a little leather thong. He
stooped over and tied it around the old dog's neck. All
25 the men except Candy watched him. "Come boy. Come
on, boy," he said gently. And he said apologetically to
Candy, "He won't even feel it." Candy did not move
nor answer him. He twitched the thong. "Come on,

---

8 **Luger:** bekannte Pistolenmarke.
18 **reversal:** Widerspruch; Umkehrung der Situation.
23 **thong:** Riemen.

boy." The old dog got slowly and stiffly to his feet and
followed the gently pulling leash.

Slim said, "Carlson."

"Yeah?"

5 "You know what to do."

"What ya mean, Slim?"

"Take a shovel," said Slim shortly.

"Oh, sure! I get you." He led the dog out into the
darkness.

10 George followed to the door and shut the door and set
the latch gently in its place. Candy lay rigidly on his bed
staring at the ceiling.

Slim said loudly, "One of my lead mules got a bad hoof.
Got to get some tar on it." His voice trailed off. It was

15 silent outside. Carlson's footsteps died away. The silence came into the room. And the silence lasted.

George chuckled, "I bet Lennie's right out there in the
barn with his pup. He won't want to come in here no
more now he's got a pup."

20 Slim said, "Candy, you can have any one of them pups
you want."

Candy did not answer. The silence fell on the room
again. It came out of the night and invaded the room.

George said, "Anybody like to play a little euchre?"

25 "I'll play out a few with you," said Whit.

---

2 **leash:** (Hunde-)Leine.
8 **to get** (infml.): verstehen.
11 **rigidly** (adv.): starr, steif.
13 **lead mule:** Leitmaultier.
14 **tar:** Teer.
   to trail off: verstummen.
24 **euchre:** populäres Kartenspiel für zwei, drei oder vier Personen.

They took places opposite each other at the table under the light, but George did not shuffle the cards. He rippled the edge of the deck nervously, and the little snapping noise drew the eyes of all the men in the room,

5 so that he stopped doing it. The silence fell on the room again. A minute passed, and another minute. Candy lay still, staring at the ceiling. Slim gazed at him for a moment and then looked down at his hands; he subdued one hand with the other, and held it down. There came

10 a little gnawing sound from under the floor and all the men looked down toward it gratefully. Only Candy continued to stare at the ceiling.

"Sounds like there was a rat under there," said George. "We ought to get a trap down there."

15 Whit broke out, "What the hell's takin' him so long? Lay out some cards, why don't you? We ain't going to get no euchre played this way."

George brought the cards together tightly and studied the backs of them. The silence was in the room

20 again.

A shot sounded in the distance. The men looked quickly at the old man. Every head turned toward him.

For a moment he continued to stare at the ceiling. Then he rolled slowly over and faced the wall and lay silent.

25 George shuffled the cards noisily and dealt them. Whit drew a scoring board to him and set the pegs to start.

---

2 f. **He rippled the edge of the deck nervously:** Er strich nervös mit dem Daumen über die Seite des Kartenstapels.

8 **to subdue:** niederhalten.

26 **scoring board:** Brett zum Festhalten von erreichten Punkten (beim *euchre* hat jeder Spielgewinn einen bestimmten Punktwert).
peg: (Holz-)Stift (um auf dem *scoring board* die Punktzahlen festzuhalten).

Whit said, "I guess you guys really come here to work."

"How do ya mean?" George asked.

Whit laughed. "Well, ya come on a Friday. You got two
5 days to work till Sunday."

"I don't see how you figure," said George.

Whit laughed again. "You do if you been around these
big ranches much. Guy that wants to look over a ranch
comes in Sat'day afternoon. He gets Sat'day night sup-
10 per an' three meals on Sunday, and he can quit Monday
mornin' after breakfast without turning his hand. But
you come to work Friday noon. You got to put in a day
an' a half no matter how you figure."

George looked at him levelly. "We're gonna stick
15 aroun' a while," he said. "Me an' Lennie's gonna roll up
a stake."

The door opened quietly and the stable buck put in his
head; a lean negro head, lined with pain, the eyes
patient. "Mr. Slim."

20 Slim took his eyes from old Candy. "Huh? Oh! Hello,
Crooks. What's'a matter?"

"You told me to warm up tar for that mule's foot. I got
it warm."

"Oh! Sure, Crooks. I'll come right out an' put it
25 on."

"I can do it if you want, Mr. Slim."

"No. I'll come do it myself." He stood up.

Crooks said, "Mr. Slim."

"Yeah."

---

14 f. **to stick around** (infml.): (in der Nähe) bleiben, herumhängen.
15 **to roll up** (slang): anhäufen, ‚zusammenkratzen'.
18 **lined:** faltig, zerfurcht.

66

"That big new guy's messin' around your pups out in the barn."

"Well, he ain't doin' no harm. I give him one of them pups."

5 "Just thought I'd tell ya," said Crooks. "He's takin' em outa the nest and handlin' them. That won't do them no good."

"He won't hurt 'em," said Slim. "I'll come along with you now."

10 George looked up. "If that crazy bastard's foolin' around too much, jus' kick him out, Slim."

Slim followed the stable buck out of the room.

George dealt and Whit picked up his cards and examined them. "Seen the new kid yet?" he asked.

15 "What kid?" George asked.

"Why, Curley's new wife."

"Yeah, I seen her."

"Well, ain't she a looloo?"

"I ain't seen that much of her," said George.

20 Whit laid down his cards impressively. "Well, stick around an' keep your eyes open. You'll see plenty. She ain't concealin' nothing. I never seen nobody like her. She got the eye goin' all the time on everybody. I bet she even gives the stable buck the eye. I don't know 25 what the hell she wants."

George asked casually, "Been any trouble since she got here?"

It was obvious that Whit was not interested in his cards. He laid his hand down and George scooped it in.

---

18 **looloo** (slang): dufte ‚Biene‘, steiler ‚Zahn‘.
29 **to scoop in:** zusammenraffen.

George laid out his deliberate solitaire hand – seven
cards, and six on top, and five on top of those.

Whit said, "I see what you mean. No, they ain't been
nothing yet. Curley's got yella-jackets in his drawers,
5 but that's all so far. Ever' time the guys is around she
shows up. She's lookin' for Curley, or she thought she
lef' somethin' layin' around and she's lookin' for it.
Seems like she can't keep away from guys. An' Curley's
pants is just crawlin' with ants, but they ain't nothing
10 come of it yet."

George said, "She's gonna make a mess. They's gonna
be a bad mess about her. She's a jail bait all set on the
trigger. That Curley got his work cut out for him. Ranch
with a bunch of guys on it ain't no place for a girl,
15 specially like her."

Whit said, "If you got idears, you oughtta come in town
with us guys tomorra night."

"Why? What's doin'?"

"Jus' the usual thing. We go in to old Susy's place. Hell
20 of a nice place. Old Susy's a laugh – always crackin'
jokes. Like she says when we come up on the front
porch las' Sat'day night. Susy opens the door and then
she yells over her shoulder, 'Get yor coats on, girls,
here comes the sheriff.' She never talks dirty, neither.
25 Got five girls there."

---

4 **yella-jackets** (slang): ›Wespen‹.
  drawers (infml., pl.): Unterhose.
11 **to make a mess** (infml.): Durcheinander anrichten.
12 f. **all set on the trigger** (infml.): ständig auf Unheil aus (*trigger:*
  [Pistolen-]Abzug).
16 **idears** (dial.): *ideas.*
20 f. **to crack jokes:** Witze reißen.
22 **porch:** Veranda (AE).

68

"What's it set you back?" George asked.

"Two an' a half. You can get a shot for two bits. Susy got nice chairs to set in, too. If a guy don't want a flop, why he can just set in the chairs and have a couple or three shots and pass the time of day and Susy don't give a damn. She ain't rushin' guys through and kickin' 'em out if they don't want a flop."

"Might go in and look the joint over," said George.

"Sure. Come along. It's a hell of a lot of fun – her crackin' jokes all the time. Like she says one time, she says, 'I've knew people that if they got a rag rug on the floor an' a kewpie doll lamp on the phonograph they think they're running a parlor house.' That's Clara's house she's talkin' about. An' Susy says, 'I know what you boys want,' she says. 'My girls is clean,' she says, 'an' there ain't no water in my whisky,' she says. 'If any you guys wanta look at a kewpie doll lamp an' take your own chance gettin' burned, why you know where to go.' An' she says, 'There's guys around here walkin' bow-legged 'cause they like to look at a kewpie doll lamp.'"

---

1 **What's it set you back?** (slang): Wieviel muß man dafür locker-
machen, was kostet einen das?

2 **a shot** (slang): einen Whisky pur (impliziert das Trinken auf ex).

3 **flop** (slang): hier: billige Übernachtung (inklusive der Dienste einer
der Damen); ‚Nummer‘.

8 **joint** (slang): Kneipe, ›Laden‹.

12 **kewpie doll:** pausbackige (Porzellan-)Puppe mit Haarknoten (Verballhornung von *cupid:* Cupido [Figur des römischen Gottes der
Liebe]).
phonograph (AE): Plattenspieler.

13 **parlor house** (slang): Bordell.

18 **to get burned** (slang): sich den Tripper holen.

19 f. **bow-legged:** O-beinig (wegen der Geschlechtskrankheit).

George asked, "Clara runs the other house, huh?"

"Yeah," said Whit. "We don't never go there. Clara gets three bucks a crack and thirty-five cents a shot, and she don't crack no jokes. But Susy's place is clean and she got nice chairs. Don't let no goo-goos in, neither."

"Me an' Lennie's rollin' up a stake," said George. "I might go in an' set and have a shot, but I ain't puttin' out no two and a half."

"Well, a guy got to have some fun sometime," said Whit.

The door opened and Lennie and Carlson came in together. Lennie crept to his bunk and sat down, trying not to attract attention. Carlson reached under his bunk and brought out his bag. He didn't look at old Candy, who still faced the wall. Carlson found a little cleaning rod in the bag and a can of oil. He laid them on his bed and then brought out the pistol, took out the magazine and snapped the loaded shell from the chamber. Then he fell to cleaning the barrel with the little rod. When the ejector snapped, Candy turned over and looked for a moment at the gun before he turned back to the wall again.

Carlson said casually, "Curley been in yet?"

"No," said Whit. "What's eatin' on Curley?"

---

3 **crack** (vulg.): hier: Fick.
5 **goo-goo** (slang): Eingeborener, Farbiger (hier wohl auf Mexikaner bezogen).
8 f. **to put out** (slang): (Geld) hinauswerfen, verpulvern.
16 f. **cleaning rod:** (Pistolen-)Laufputzer.
20 **barrel:** (Pistolen-)Lauf.
21 **ejector:** Auswerfer (bei Schußwaffen).
25 **What's eatin' on Curley?** (slang): Welche Laus ist C. über die Leber gelaufen?

Carlson squinted down the barrel of his gun. "Lookin'
for his old lady. I seen him going round and round
outside."

Whit said sarcastically, "He spends half his time lookin'
5 for her, and the rest of the time she's lookin' for
him."

Curley burst into the room excitely. "Any you guys
seen my wife?" he demanded.

"She ain't been here," said Whit.

10 Curley looked threateningly about the room. "Where
the hell's Slim?"

"Went out in the barn," said George. "He was gonna
put some tar on a split hoof."

Curley's shoulders dropped and squared. "How long
15 ago'd he go?"

"Five – ten minutes."

Curley jumped out the door and banged it after
him.

Whit stood up. "I guess maybe I'd like to see this," he
20 said. "Curley's just spoilin' or he wouldn't start for
Slim. An' Curley's handy, God damn handy. Got in the
finals for the Golden Gloves. He got newspaper clippings about it." He considered. "But jus' the same, he
better leave Slim alone. Nobody don't know what Slim
25 can do."

"Thinks Slim's with his wife, don't he?" said George.

---

4 **sarcastically** (adv.): sarkastisch.
17 **to bang:** (laut) zuschlagen.
20 **to spoil:** hier: (auf einen Streit) ‚brennen‘, versessen sein.
22 **Golden Gloves:** wörtl.: »Goldene Handschuhe« (1927 von der *New York Daily News* ins Leben gerufener Amateurboxwettbewerb).
22f. **newspaper clippings:** Zeitungsausschnitte.

"Looks like it," Whit said. "'Course Slim ain't. Least I don't think Slim is. But I like to see the fuss if it comes off. Come on, le's go."

George said, "I'm stayin' right here. I don't want to get mixed up in nothing. Lennie and me got to make a stake."

Carlson finished the cleaning of the gun and put it in the bag and pushed the bag under his bunk. "I guess I'll go out and look her over," he said. Old Candy lay still, and Lennie, from his bunk, watched George cautiously.

When Whit and Carlson were gone and the door closed after them, George turned to Lennie. "What you got on your mind?"

"I ain't done nothing, George. Slim says I better not pet them pups so much for a while. Slim says it ain't good for them; so I come right in. I been good, George."

"I coulda told you that," said George.

"Well, I wasn't hurtin' 'em none. I jus' had mine in my lap pettin' it."

George asked, "Did you see Slim out in the barn?"

"Sure I did. He tol' me I better not pet that pup no more."

"Did you see that girl?"

"You mean Curley's girl?"

"Yeah. Did she come in the barn?"

"No. Anyways I never seen her."

"You never seen Slim talkin' to her?"

"Uh-uh. She ain't been in the barn."

"O. K.," said George. "I guess them guys ain't gonna

---

2 **fuss** (infml.): Theater, Wirbel, Trara.
2f. **if it comes off** (infml.): wenn es dazu kommt, wenn es hinhaut.
4f. **to get mixed up in s.th.:** in etwas verwickelt werden.

see no fight. If there's any fightin', Lennie, you keep
out of it."

"I don't want no fights," said Lennie. He got up from
his bunk and sat down at the table, across from George.
5 Almost automatically George shuffled the cards and
laid out his solitaire hand. He used a deliberate,
thoughtful slowness.

Lennie reached for a face card and studied it, then
turned it upside down and studied it. "Both ends the
10 same," he said. "George, why is it both ends the
same?"

"I don't know," said George. "That's jus' the way they
make 'em. What was Slim doin' in the barn when you
seen him?"

15 "Slim?"

"Sure. You seen him in the barn, an' he tol' you not to
pet the pups so much."

"Oh, yeah. He had a can a' tar an' a paint brush. I don't
know what for."

20 "You sure that girl didn't come in like she come in here
today?"

"No. She never come."

George sighed. "You give me a good whore house every
time," he said. "A guy can go in an' get drunk and get
25 ever'thing outa his system all at once, an' no messes.
And he knows how much it's gonna set him back. These
here jail baits is just set on the trigger of the hoosegow."

---

8 **face card:** Bildkarte (As, König usw.)
23 **whore house** (slang): Hurenhaus, Bordell.
24 f. **to get s.th. out of one's system:** etwas loswerden, sich etwas von
der Leber reden.
28 **hoosegow** (slang): Knast (von span. *juzgado* ›Gefängnis‹).

Lennie followed his words admiringly, and moved his lips a little to keep up. George continued, "You remember Andy Cushman, Lennie? Went to grammar school?"

5 "The one that his old lady used to make hot cakes for the kids?" Lennie asked.

"Yeah. That's the one. You can remember anything if there's anything to eat in it." George looked carefully at the solitaire hand. He put an ace up on his scoring 10 rack and piled a two, three and four of diamonds on it. "Andy's in San Quentin right now on account of a tart," said George.

Lennie drummed on the table with his fingers. "George?"

15 "Huh?"

"George, how long's it gonna be till we get that little place an' live on the fatta the lan'– an' rabbits?"

"I don't know," said George. "We gotta get a big stake together. I know a little place we can get cheap, but 20 they ain't givin' it away."

Old Candy turned slowly over. His eyes were wide open. He watched George carefully.

Lennie said, "Tell about that place, George."

"I jus' tol' you, jus' las' night."

25 "Go on – tell again, George."

"Well, it's ten acres," said George. "Got a little win'-

---

5 **that his** (dial.): *whose.*
 hot cakes (AE, pl.): Pfannkuchen, Maiskuchen.
9 f. **scoring rack:** vertikale Reihe, in der die Karten in der Reihenfolge ihres Punktwertes aufeinandergelegt werden.
10 **diamonds** (pl.): Karo (Spielkartenfarbe).
11 **San Quentin:** kalifornisches Hochsicherheitsgefängnis nördlich von San Francisco.

74

mill. Got a little shack on it, an' a chicken run. Got a
kitchen, orchard, cherries, apples, peaches, 'cots, nuts,
got a few berries. They's a place for alfalfa and plenty
water to flood it. They's a pig pen —"

5 "An' rabbits, George."

"No place for rabbits now, but I could easy build a few
hutches and you could feed alfalfa to the rabbits."

"Damn right, I could," said Lennie. "You God damn
right I could."

10 George's hands stopped working with the cards. His
voice was growing warmer. "An' we could have a few
pigs. I could build a smoke house like the one gran'pa
had, an' when we kill a pig we can smoke the bacon and
the hams, and make sausage an' all like that. An' when

15 the salmon run up river we could catch a hundred of 'em
an' salt 'em down or smoke 'em. We could have them
for breakfast. They ain't nothing so nice as smoked
salmon. When the fruit come in we could can it – and
tomatoes, they're easy to can. Ever' Sunday we'd kill a

20 chicken or a rabbit. Maybe we'd have a cow or a goat,
and the cream is so God damn thick you got to cut it
with a knife and take it out with a spoon."

Lennie watched him with wide eyes, and old Candy
watched him too. Lennie said softly, "We could live offa

25 the fatta the lan'."

---

1 **shack:** Schuppen.
  chicken run: Hühnerfreilauf, -hof.
2 **'cots** (infml.): Kurzform für *apricots:* Aprikosen.
3 **alfalfa:** Alfalfa (Luzernenart).
4 **pig pen** (AE): Schweinestall.
12 **smoke house:** Räucherkammer.
15 **salmon:** Lachs.

"Sure," said George. "All kin's a vegetables in the garden, and if we want a little whisky we can sell a few eggs or something, or some milk. We'd jus' live there. We'd belong there. There wouldn't be no more runnin'
5 round the country and gettin' fed by a Jap cook. No, sir, we'd have our own place where we belonged and not sleep in no bunkhouse."

"Tell about the house, George," Lennie begged.

"Sure, we'd have a little house an' a room to ourself.
10 Little fat iron stove, an' in the winter we'd keep a fire goin' in it. It ain't enough land so we'd have to work too hard. Maybe six, seven hours a day. We wouldn't have to buck no barley eleven hours a day. An' when we put in a crop, why, we'd be there to take the crop up. We'd
15 know what come of our planting."

"An' rabbits," Lennie said eagerly. "An' I'd take care of 'em. Tell how I'd do that, George."

"Sure, you'd go out in the alfalfa patch an' you'd have a sack. You'd fill up the sack and bring it in an' put it in
20 the rabbit cages."

"They'd nibble an' they'd nibble," said Lennie, "the way they do. I seen 'em."

"Ever' six weeks or so," George continued, "them does would throw a litter so we'd have plenty rabbits to eat
25 an' to sell. An' we'd keep a few pigeons to go flyin' around the win'mill like they done when I was a kid."

He looked raptly at the wall over Lennie's head. "An'

---

1 **kin's a** (dial.): *kinds of.*
5 **Jap** (infml.): *Japanese.*
10 **fat:** hier: wohlbestückt, gut beheizt.
21 **to nibble:** (herum)nagen.
23 **doe:** Häsin.
27 **raptly** (adv.): verzückt.

it'd be our own, an' nobody could can us. If we don't like a guy we can say, 'Get the hell out,' and by God he's got to do it. An' if a fren' come along, why we'd have an extra bunk, an' we'd say, 'Why don't you spen' the night?' an' by God he would. We'd have a setter dog and a couple stripe cats, but you gotta watch out them cats don't get the little rabbits."

Lennie breathed hard. "You jus' let 'em try to get the rabbits. I'll break their God damn necks. I'll ... I'll smash 'em with a stick." He subsided, grumbling to himself, threatening the future cats which might dare to disturb the future rabbits.

George sat entranced with his own picture.

When Candy spoke they both jumped as though they had been caught doing something reprehensible. Candy said, "You know where's a place like that?"

George was on guard immediately. "S'pose I do," he said. "What's that to you?"

"You don't need to tell me where it's at. Might be any place."

"Sure," said George. "That's right. You couldn't find it in a hundred years."

Candy went on excitedly, "How much they want for a place like that?"

George watched him suspiciously. "Well – I could get it

---

3 **fren'** (dial.): *friend.*
5 **setter dog:** Setter (Hunderasse).
10 **to smash:** zerschmettern.
   to subside: verstummen.
13 **entranced:** verzückt.
15 **reprehensible:** verwerflich.
17 **on guard:** vorsichtig, auf der Hut.
19 **to tell s.o. where it's at** (slang): jdm. sagen, was Sache ist.

for six hundred bucks. The ol' people that owns it is flat bust an' the ol' lady needs an operation. Say – what's it to you? You got nothing to do with us."

Candy said, "I ain't much good with on'y one hand. I
5 lost my hand right here on this ranch. That's why they give me a job swampin'. An' they give me two hunderd an' fifty dollars 'cause I los' my hand. An' I got fifty more saved up right in the bank, right now. Tha's three hunderd, and I got fifty more comin' the end a the
10 month. Tell you what —" He leaned forward eagerly. "S'pose I went in with you guys. Tha's three hunderd an' fifty bucks I'd put in. I ain't much good, but I could cook and tend the chickens and hoe the garden some. How'd that be?"

15 George half-closed his eyes. "I gotta think about that. We was always gonna do it by ourselves."

Candy interrupted him, "I'd make a will an' leave my share to you guys in case I kick off, 'cause I ain't got no relatives nor nothing. You guys got any money? Maybe
20 we could do her right now?"

George spat on the floor disgustedly. "We got ten bucks between us." Then he said thoughtfully, "Look, if me an' Lennie work a month an' don't spen' nothing, we'll have a hunderd bucks. That'd be four fifty. I bet we
25 could swing her for that. Then you an' Lennie could go get her started an' I'd get a job an' make up the res', an' you could sell eggs an' stuff like that."

---

1 f. **flat bust** (slang): total pleite.
6 **hunderd** (dial.): *hundred.*
13 **to hoe:** hacken, harken.
   some (adv., AE): ein bißchen.
18 **to kick off** (slang): ‚abkratzen'.
25 **to swing s.o.** (infml.): jdn. rumkriegen, (zu etwas) überreden.

They fell into a silence. They looked at one another, amazed. This thing they had never really believed in was coming true. George said reverently, "Jesus Christ! I bet we could swing her." His eyes were full of wonder.
5 "I bet we could swing her," he repeated softly.
Candy sat on the edge of his bunk. He scratched the stump of his wrist nervously. "I got hurt four year ago," he said. "They'll can me purty soon. Jus' as soon as I can't swamp out no bunkhouses they'll put me on the
10 county. Maybe if I give you guys my money, you'll let me hoe in the garden even after I ain't no good at it. An' I'll wash dishes an' little chicken stuff like that. But I'll be on our own place, an' I'll be let to work on our own place." He said miserably, "You seen what they done to
15 my dog tonight? They says he wasn't no good to himself nor nobody else. When they can me here I wisht somebody'd shoot me. But they won't do nothing like that. I won't have no place to go, an' I can't get no more jobs. I'll have thirty dollars more comin', time you guys is
20 ready to quit."
George stood up. "We'll do her," he said. "We'll fix up that little old place an' we'll go live there." He sat down again. They all sat still, all bemused by the beauty of the thing, each mind was popped into the future when this
25 lovely thing should come about.
George said wonderingly, "S'pose they was a carnival or

---

7 **stump:** Stumpf.
9 f. **to put s.o. on the county** (slang): jdn. auf die Straße setzen (so daß er von der Sozialhilfe abhängig ist).
21 **we'll do her** (slang): wir werden die Sache schon schaukeln.
to fix up (infml.): herrichten, aufmöbeln.
23 **bemused:** verwirrt, durcheinander.
26 **carnival:** Volksfest, Jahrmarkt.

a circus come to town, or a ball game, or any damn thing." Old Candy nodded in appreciation of the idea. "We'd just go to her," George said. "We wouldn't ask nobody if we could. Jus' say, 'We'll go to her,' an' we
5 would. Jus' milk the cow and sling some grain to the chickens an' go to her."

"An' put some grass to the rabbits," Lennie broke in. "I wouldn't never forget to feed them. When we gon'ta do it, George?"

10 "In one month. Right squack in one month. Know what I'm gon'ta do? I'm gon'ta write to them old people that owns the place that we'll take it. An' Candy'll send a hunderd dollars to bind her."

"Sure will," said Candy. "They got a good stove
15 there?"

"Sure, got a nice stove, burns coal or wood."

"I'm gonna take my pup," said Lennie. "I bet by Christ he likes it there, by Jesus."

Voices were approaching from outside. George said
20 quickly, "Don't tell nobody about it. Jus' us three an' nobody else. They li'ble to can us so we can't make no stake. Jus' go on like we was gonna buck barley the rest of our lives, then all of a sudden some day we'll go get our pay an' scram outa here."

25 Lennie and Candy nodded, and they were grinning with delight. "Don't tell nobody," Lennie said to himself.

Candy said, "George."

"Huh?"

---

8 **gon'ta** (dial.): *going to.*
10 **squack** (slang): etwa: haargenau (emphatisches Füllsel).
21 **to be liable to do s.th.:** hier: es fertigkriegen, etwas zu tun.

"I ought to of shot that dog myself, George. I shouldn't ought to of let no stranger shoot my dog."

The door opened. Slim came in, followed by Curley and Carlson and Whit. Slim's hands were black with tar and he was scowling. Curley hung close to his elbow.

Curley said, "Well, I didn't mean nothing. Slim. I just ast you."

Slim said, "Well, you been askin' me too often. I'm gettin' God damn sick of it. If you can't look after your own God damn wife, what you expect me to do about it? You lay offa me."

"I'm jus' tryin' to tell you I didn't mean nothing," said Curley. "I jus' thought you might of saw her."

"Why'n't you tell her to stay the hell home where she belongs?" said Carlson. "You let her hang around bunkhouses and pretty soon you're gonna have som'pin on your hands and you won't be able to do nothing about it."

Curley whirled on Carlson. "You keep outa this les' you wanta step outside."

Carlson laughed. "You God damn punk," he said. "You tried to throw a scare into Slim, an' you couldn't make it stick. Slim throwed a scare into you. You're yella as a frog belly. I don't care if you're the best welter in the country. You come for me, an' I'll kick your God damn head off."

Candy joined the attack with joy. "Glove fulla vaseline," he said disgustedly. Curley glared at him. His eyes slipped on past and lighted on Lennie; and Lennie

---

11 **to lay off s.o.** (slang): jdn. in Ruhe lassen.
16 **som'pin** (dial.): *something*.
22 **to throw a scare into s.o.** (infml.): jdn. einschüchtern.
24 **welter:** Weltergewicht (Gewichtsklasse beim Boxen bis 66,67 kg).

was still smiling with delight at the memory of the ranch.

Curley stepped over to Lennie like a terrier. "What the hell you laughin' at?"

5 Lennie looked blankly at him. "Huh?"

Then Curley's rage exploded. "Come on, ya big bastard. Get up on your feet. No big son-of-a-bitch is gonna laugh at me. I'll show ya who's yella."

Lennie looked helplessly at George, and then he got up
10 and tried to retreat. Curley was balanced and poised. He slashed at Lennie with his left, and then smashed down his nose with a right. Lennie gave a cry of terror. Blood welled from his nose. "George," he cried. "Make 'um let me alone, George." He backed until he was
15 against the wall, and Curley followed, slugging him in the face. Lennie's hands remained at his sides; he was too frightened to defend himself.

George was on his feet yelling, "Get him, Lennie. Don't let him do it."

20 Lennie covered his face with his huge paws and bleated with terror. He cried, "Make 'um stop, George." Then Curley attacked his stomach and cut off his wind.

Slim jumped up. "The dirty little rat," he cried, "I'll get 'um myself."

25 George put out his hand and grabbed Slim. "Wait a minute," he shouted. He cupped his hands around his mouth and yelled, "Get 'im, Lennie!"

10 **poised:** gelassen, die Ruhe selbst; kampfbereit.
11 **to slash:** schlagen.
13 **to well:** quellen.
15f. **to slug s.o. in the face** (infml.): jdm. eine reindreschen.
20 **to bleat:** blöken, brüllen.
26f. **to cup one's hands around one's mouth:** die Hände (trichterförmig) um den Mund legen.

82

Lennie took his hands away from his face and looked about for George, and Curley slashed at his eyes. The big face was covered with blood. George yelled again, "I said get him."

5 Curley's fist was swinging when Lennie reached for it. The next minute Curley was flopping like a fish on a line, and his closed fist was lost in Lennie's big hand. George ran down the room. "Leggo of him, Lennie. Let go."

10 But Lennie watched in terror the flopping little man whom he held. Blood ran down Lennie's face, one of his eyes was cut and closed. George slapped him in the face again and again, and still Lennie held on to the closed fist. Curley was white and shrunken by now, and his
15 struggling had become weak. He stood crying, his fist lost in Lennie's paw.

George shouted over and over. "Leggo his hand, Lennie. Leggo. Slim, come help me while the guy got any hand left."

20 Suddenly Lennie let go his hold. He crouched cowering against the wall. "You tol' me to, George," he said miserably.

Curley sat down on the floor, looking in wonder at his crushed hand. Slim and Carlson bent over him. Then
25 Slim straightened up and regarded Lennie with horror. "We got to get him in to a doctor," he said. "Looks to me like ever' bone in his han' is bust."

"I didn't wanta," Lennie cried. "I didn't wanta hurt him."

---

6 **to flop:** zappeln.
8 **leggo** (dial.): *let go.*
14 **shrunken:** in sich zusammengesunken.
20 **cowering:** geduckt, kauernd.

Slim said, "Carlson, you get the candy wagon hitched up. We'll take 'um into Soledad an' get 'um fixed up." Carlson hurried out. Slim turned to the whimpering Lennie. "It ain't your fault," he said. "This punk sure
5 had it comin' to him. But – Jesus! He ain't hardly got no han' left." Slim hurried out, and in a moment returned with a tin cup of water. He held it to Curley's lips.
George said, "Slim, will we get canned now? We need the stake. Will Curley's old man can us now?"
10 Slim smiled wryly. He knelt down beside Curley. "You got your senses in hand enough to listen?" he asked. Curley nodded. "Well, then listen," Slim went on. "I think you got your han' caught in a machine. If you don't tell nobody what happened, we ain't going to. But
15 you jus' tell an' try to get this guy canned and we'll tell ever'body, an' then will you get the laugh."
"I won't tell," said Curley. He avoided looking at Lennie.
Buggy wheels sounded outside. Slim helped Curley up.
20 "Come on now. Carlson's gonna take you to a doctor." He helped Curley out the door. The sound of wheels drew away. In a moment Slim came back into the bunkhouse. He looked at Lennie, still crouched fearfully against the wall. "Le's see your hands," he
25 asked.
Lennie stuck out his hands.

---

1 **candy wagon** (slang): bequemer Einspänner.
1 f. **to hitch up:** anschirren, anspannen.
4 **sure** (adv., AE): ganz bestimmt, todsicher.
5 **had it coming to him** (infml.): hat sich das selber zuzuschreiben.
10 **wryly** (adv.): ironisch, hämisch.
19 **buggy:** ieichter Einspänner.

"Christ awmighty, I hate to have you mad at me," Slim said.

George broke in, "Lennie was jus' scairt," he explained. "He didn't know what to do. I told you nobody ought never to fight him. No, I guess it was Candy I told."

Candy nodded solemnly. "That's jus' what you done," he said. "Right this morning when Curley first lit intil your fren', you says, 'He better not fool with Lennie if he knows what's good for 'um.' That's jus' what you says to me."

George turned to Lennie. "It ain't your fault," he said. "You don't need to be scairt no more. You done jus' what I tol' you to. Maybe you better go in the wash room an' clean up your face. You look like hell."

Lennie smiled with his bruised mouth. "I didn't want no trouble," he said. He walked toward the door, but just before he came to it, he turned back. "George?"

"What you want?"

"I can still tend the rabbits, George?"

"Sure. You ain't done nothing wrong."

"I di'n't mean no harm, George."

"Well, get the hell out and wash your face."

Four

Crooks, the Negro stable buck, had his bunk in the harness room; a little shed that leaned off the wall of the barn. On one side of the little room there was a square

---

8 **to light intil** (= *into*) **s.o.** (dial.): jdn. angreifen, auf jdn. losgehen.
16 **bruised:** mit Blutergüssen bedeckt, zerschlagen.

four-paned window, and on the other, a narrow plank
door leading into the barn. Crooks' bunk was a long box
filled with straw, on which his blankets were flung. On
the wall by the window there were pegs on which hung
5 broken harness in process of being mended; strips of
new leather; and under the window itself a little bench
for leather-working tools, curved knives and needles
and balls of linen thread, and a small hand riveter. On
pegs were also pieces of harness, a split collar with the
10 horsehair stuffing sticking out, a broken hame, and a
trace chain with its leather covering split. Crooks had
his apple box over his bunk, and in it a range of
medicine bottles, both for himself and for the horses.
There were cans of saddle soap and a drippy can of tar
15 with its paint brush sticking over the edge. And scattered about the floor were a number of personal possessions; for, being alone, Crooks could leave his things
about, and being a stable buck and a cripple, he was
more permanent than the other men, and he had
20 accumulated more possessions than he could carry on
his back.
Crooks possessed several pairs of shoes, a pair of rubber
boots, a big alarm clock and a single-barreled shotgun.
And he had books, too; a tattered dictionary and a
25 mauled copy of the California civil code for 1905. There

---

8 **hand riveter:** Handnietmaschine (*rivet:* Niete).
9 **collar:** hier: Kumt, Kummet (gepolsterter Bügel um den Hals von
   Zugtieren).
10 **hame:** Kummetfeder, -holz (Teil des Zaumzeugs bei Zugtieren).
24 **tattered:** zerfleddert.
25 **mauled:** übel zugerichtet.
   civil code: Bürgerliches Gesetzbuch.

were battered magazines and a few dirty books on a special shelf over his bunk. A pair of large gold-rimmed spectacles hung from a nail on the wall above his bed.

5 This room was swept and fairly neat, for Crooks was a proud, aloof man. He kept his distance and demanded that other people keep theirs. His body was bent over to the left by his crooked spine, and his eyes lay deep in his head, and because of their depth seemed to glitter with
10 intensity. His lean face was lined with deep black wrinkles, and he had thin, pain-tightened lips which were lighter than his face.

It was Saturday night. Through the open door that led into the barn came the sound of moving horses, of feet
15 stirring, of teeth champing on hay, of the rattle of halter chains. In the stable buck's room a small electric globe threw a meager yellow light.

Crooks sat on his bunk. His shirt was out of his jeans in back. In one hand he held a bottle of liniment, and with
20 the other he rubbed his spine. Now and then he poured a few drops of the liniment into his pink-palmed hand and reached up under his shirt to rub again. He flexed his muscles against his back and shivered.

---

1 **battered:** ramponiert.
2 **gold-rimmed:** mit einem Goldrand.
6 **aloof:** unnahbar.
8 **spine:** Rückgrat, Wirbelsäule.
15 **to champ:** mampfen, laut kauen.
15f. **halter chain:** Halfterkette.
16 **globe:** (Glüh-)Birne.
17 **meager:** spärlich, schwach.
22f. **to flex one's muscles:** seine Muskeln spielen lassen.
23 **to shiver:** (er)zittern, schaudern.

Noiselessly Lennie appeared in the open doorway and stood there looking in, his big shoulders nearly filling the opening. For a moment Crooks did not see him, but on raising his eyes he stiffened and a scowl came on his
5 face. His hand came out from under his shirt.

Lennie smiled helplessly in an attempt to make friends.

Crooks said sharply, "You got no right to come in my room. This here's my room. Nobody got any right in
10 here but me."

Lennie gulped and his smile grew more fawning. "I ain't doing nothing," he said. "Just come to look at my puppy. And I seen your light," he explained.

"Well, I got a right to have a light. You go on get outa
15 my room. I ain't wanted in the bunkhouse, and you ain't wanted in my room."

"Why ain't you wanted?" Lennie asked.

"'Cause I'm black. They play cards in there, but I can't play because I'm black. They say I stink. Well, I tell
20 you, you all of you stink to me."

Lennie flapped his big hands helplessly. "Ever'body went into town," he said. "Slim an' George an' ever'-body. George says I gotta stay here an' not get in no trouble. I seen your light."

25 "Well, what do you want?"

"Nothing – I seen your light. I thought I could jus' come in an' set."

Crooks stared at Lennie, and he reached behind him

---

4 **scowl:** finstere Miene.
11 **fawning:** einschmeichelnd, kriecherisch.
21 **to flap:** hier: schlenkern.

and took down the spectacles and adjusted them over his pink ears and stared again. "I don't know what you're doin' in the barn anyway," he complained. "You ain't no skinner. They's no call for a bucker to come
5 into the barn at all. You ain't no skinner. You ain't got nothing to do with the horses."

"The pup," Lennie repeated. "I come to see my pup."

"Well, go see your pup, then. Don't come in a place
10 where you're not wanted."

Lennie lost his smile. He advanced a step into the room, then remembered and backed to the door again. "I looked at 'em a little. Slim says I ain't to pet 'em very much."

15 Crooks said, "Well, you been takin' 'em out of the nest all the time. I wonder the old lady don't move 'em someplace else."

"Oh, she don't care. She lets me." Lennie had moved into the room again.

20 Crooks scowled, but Lennie's disarming smile defeated him. "Come on in and set a while," Crooks said. "'Long as you won't get out and leave me alone, you might as well set down." His tone was a little more friendly. "All the boys gone into town, huh?"

25 "All but old Candy. He just sets in the bunkhouse sharpening his pencil and sharpening and figuring."

Crooks adjusted his glasses. "Figuring? What's Candy figuring about?"

Lennie almost shouted, "'Bout the rabbits."

---

1 **to adjust:** zurechtrücken.
4 f. **They's** (= *there's*) **no call for ... into the barn:** Ein Getreidepacker hat im Stall nichts zu suchen.

"You're nuts," said Crooks. "You're crazy as a wedge. What rabbits you talkin' about?"

"The rabbits we're gonna get, and I get to tend 'em, cut grass an' give 'em water, an' like that."

5 "Jus' nuts," said Crooks. "I don't blame the guy you travel with for keepin' you outa sight."

Lennie said quietly, "It ain't no lie. We're gonna do it. Gonna get a little place an' live on the fatta lan'."

10 Crooks settled himself more comfortably on his bunk. "Set down," he invited. "Set down on the nail keg."

Lennie hunched down on the little barrel. "You think it's a lie," Lennie said. "But it ain't no lie. Ever' word's the truth, an' you can ast George."

15 Crooks put his dark chin into his pink palm. "You travel aroun' with George, don't ya?"

"Sure. Me an' him goes ever' place together."

Crooks continued. "Sometimes he talks, and you don't know what the hell he's talkin' about. Ain't that so?"

20 He leaned forward, boring Lennie with his deep eyes. "Ain't that so?"

"Yeah ... sometimes."

"Jus' talks on, an' you don't know what the hell it's all about?"

25 "Yeah ... sometimes. But ... not always."

Crooks leaned forward over the edge of the bunk. "I ain't a southern Negro," he said. "I was born right here

---

1 **to be nuts** (infml.): verrückt sein, spinnen.
   crazy as a wedge (infml.): total verrückt; Basis des Vergleiches ist wohl die wortspielerisch gebrauchte Bedeutung von *to craze* ›rissig machen, spalten‹.
11 **nail keg:** Nagelfäßchen.

in California. My old man had a chicken ranch, 'bout ten acres. The white kids come to play at our place, an' sometimes I went to play with them, and some of them was pretty nice. My ol' man didn't like that. I never knew till long later why he didn't like that. But I know now." He hesitated, and when he spoke again his voice was softer. "There wasn't another colored family for miles around. And now there ain't a colored man on this ranch an' there's jus' one family in Soledad." He laughed. "If I say something, why it's just a nigger sayin' it."

Lennie asked, "How long you think it'll be before them pups will be old enough to pet?"

Crooks laughed again. "A guy can talk to you an' be sure you won't go blabbin'. Couple of weeks an' them pups'll be all right. George knows what he's about. Jus' talks, an' you don't understand nothing." He leaned forward excitely. "This is just a nigger talkin', an' a busted-back nigger. So it don't mean nothing, see? You couldn't remember it anyways. I seen it over an' over – a guy talkin' to another guy and it don't make no difference if he don't hear or understand. The thing is, they're talkin', or they're settin' still not talkin'. It don't make no difference, no difference." His excitement had increased until he pounded his knee with his hand. "George can tell you screwy things, and it don't matter. It's just the talking. It's just bein' with another guy. That's all." He paused.

His voice grew soft and persuasive. "S'pose George

---

15 **to blab** (infml.): plappern.
26 **screwy** (infml.): verrückt, exzentrisch.
29 **persuasive:** überredend.

don't come back no more. S'pose he took a powder and just ain't coming back. What'll you do then?"

Lennie's attention came gradually to what had been said. "What?" he demanded.

5 "I said s'pose George went into town tonight and you never heard of him no more." Crooks pressed forward some kind of private victory. "Just s'pose that," he repeated.

"He won't do it," Lennie cried. "George wouldn't do
10 nothing like that. I been with George a long time. He'll come back tonight —" But the doubt was too much for him. "Don't you think he will?"

Crooks' face lighted with pleasure in his torture. "Nobody can't tell what a guy'll do," he observed calmly.
15 "Le's say he wants to come back and can't. S'pose he gets killed or hurt so he can't come back."

Lennie struggled to understand. "George won't do nothing like that," he repeated. "George is careful. He won't get hurt. He ain't never been hurt, 'cause he's
20 careful."

"Well, s'pose, jus' s'pose he don't come back. What'll you do then?"

Lennie's face wrinkled with apprehension. "I don' know. Say, what you doin' anyways?" he cried. "This
25 ain't true. George ain't got hurt."

Crooks bored in on him. "Want me ta tell ya what'll happen? They'll take ya to the booby hatch. They'll tie ya up with a collar, like a dog."

---

1 **to take a powder** (slang): abhauen, eine Fliege machen.

6 **to press s.th. forward** (infml.): etwas auskosten.

23 **apprehension:** Befürchtung, Besorgnis.

27 **booby hatch** (slang): Klapsmühle, Irrenhaus.

Suddenly Lennie's eyes centered and grew quiet, and mad. He stood up and walked dangerously toward Crooks. "Who hurt George?" he demanded.

Crooks saw the danger as it approached him. He edged
5 back on his bunk to get out of the way. "I was just supposin'," he said. "George ain't hurt. He's all right. He'll be back all right."

Lennie stood over him. "What you supposin' for? Ain't nobody goin' to suppose no hurt to George."

10 Crooks removed his glasses and wiped his eyes with his fingers. "Jus' set down," he said. "George ain't hurt."

Lennie growled back to his seat on the nail keg. "Ain't nobody goin' to talk no hurt to George," he grum-
15 bled.

Crooks said gently, "Maybe you can see now. You got George. You *know* he's goin' to come back. S'pose you didn't have nobody. S'pose you couldn't go into the bunkhouse and play rummy 'cause you was black.
20 How'd you like that? S'pose you had to sit out here an' read books. Sure you could play horseshoes till it got dark, but then you got to read books. Books ain't no good. A guy needs somebody – to be near him." He whined, "A guy goes nuts if he ain't got nobody. Don't
25 make no difference who the guy is, long's he's with you. I tell ya," he cried, " I tell ya a guy gets too lonely an' he gets sick."

"George gonna come back," Lennie reassured himself

---

4 f. **to edge back:** langsam zurückrutschen.

19 **rummy:** Kartenspiel; das uns geläufige Rommé ist eine Variante von vielen.

24 **to whine:** heulen, jammern.

in a frightened voice. "Maybe George come back already. Maybe I better go see."

Crooks said, "I didn't mean to scare you. He'll come back. I was talkin' about myself. A guy sets alone out here at night, maybe readin' books or thinkin' or stuff like that. Sometimes he gets thinkin', an' he got nothing to tell him what's so an' what ain't so. Maybe if he sees somethin', he don't know whether it's right or not. He can't turn to some other guy and ast him if he sees it too. He can't tell. He got nothing to measure by. I seen things out here. I wasn't drunk. I don't know if I was asleep. If some guy was with me, he could tell me I was asleep, an' then it would be all right. But I jus' don't know." Crooks was looking across the room now, looking toward the window.

Lennie said miserably, "George wun't go away and leave me. I know George wun't do that."

The stable buck went on dreamily, "I remember when I was a little kid on my old man's chicken ranch. Had two brothers. They was always near me, always there. Used to sleep right in the same room, right in the same bed – all three. Had a strawberry patch. Had an alfalfa patch. Used to turn the chickens out in the alfalfa on a sunny morning. My brothers'd set on a fence rail an' watch 'em – white chickens they was."

Gradually Lennie's interest came around to what was being said. "George says we're gonna have alfalfa for the rabbits."

"What rabbits?"

"We're gonna have rabbits an' a berry patch."

"You're nuts."

16 **wun't** (dial.): *wouldn't.*

94

"We are too. You ast George."

"You're nuts." Crooks was scornful. "I seen hunderds of men come by on the road an' on the ranches, with their bindles on their back an' that same damn thing in their heads. Hunderds of them. They come, an' they quit an' go on; an' every damn one of 'em's got a little piece of land in his head. An' never a God damn one of 'em ever gets it. Just like heaven. Ever'body wants a little piece of lan'. I read plenty of books out here. Nobody never gets to heaven, and nobody gets no land. It's just in their head. They're all the time talkin' about it, but it's jus' in their head." He paused and looked toward the open door, for the horses were moving restlessly and the halter chains clinked. A horse whinnied. "I guess somebody's out there," Crooks said. "Maybe Slim. Slim comes in sometimes two, three times a night. Slim's a real skinner. He looks out for his team." He pulled himself painfully upright and moved toward the door. "That you, Slim?" he called.

Candy's voice answered. "Slim went in town. Say, you seen Lennie?"

"Ya mean the big guy?"

"Yeah. Seen him around any place?"

"He's in here," Crooks said shortly. He went back to his bunk and lay down.

Candy stood in the doorway scratching his bald wrist and looking blindly into the lighted room. He made no

---

1 **We are too:** 1. Und ob wir das (tun) werden (von Lennie auf seinen letzten Satz bezogen); 2. Und ob wir das sind (als unbewußt ironische Bestätigung auf Crooks' »You're nuts« zu verstehen).
14 f. **to whinny:** wiehern.
26 **bald:** kahl.

attempt to enter. "Tell ya what, Lennie. I been figuring out about them rabbits."

Crooks said irritably, "You can come in if you want."

5 Candy seemed embarrassed. "I do' know. 'Course, if ya want me to."

"Come on in. If ever'body's comin' in, you might just as well." It was difficult for Crooks to conceal his pleasure with anger.

10 Candy came in, but he was still embarrassed, "You got a nice cozy little place in here," he said to Crooks. "Must be nice to have a room all to yourself this way."

"Sure," said Crooks. "And a manure pile under the
15 window. Sure, it's swell."

Lennie broke in, "You said about them rabbits."

Candy leaned against the wall beside the broken collar while he scratched the wrist stump. "I been here a long time," he said. "An' Crooks been here a long time.
20 This's the first time I ever been in his room."

Crooks said darkly, "Guys don't come into a colored man's room very much. Nobody been here but Slim. Slim an' the boss."

Candy quickly changed the subject. "Slim's as good a
25 skinner as I ever seen."

Lennie leaned toward the old swamper. "About them rabbits," he insisted.

Candy smiled. "I got it figured out. We can make some money on them rabbits if we go about it right."

---

3 **irritably** (adv.): gereizt.
5 **embarrassed:** verlegen.
11 **cozy** (AE): gemütlich, behaglich.
14 **manure pile:** Misthaufen.

"But I get to tend 'em," Lennie broke in. "George says I get to tend 'em. He promised."

Crooks interrupted brutally. "You guys is just kiddin' yourself. You'll talk about it a hell of a lot, but you won't get no land. You'll be a swamper here till they take you out in a box. Hell, I seen too many guys. Lennie here'll quit an' be on the road in two, three weeks. Seems like ever' guy got land in his head."

Candy rubbed his cheek angrily. "You God damn right we're gonna do it. George says we are. We got the money right now."

"Yeah?" said Crooks. "An' where's George now? In town in a whore house. That's where your money's goin'. Jesus, I seen it happen too many times. I seen too many guys with land in their head. They never get none under their hand."

Candy cried, "Sure they all want it. Everybody wants a little bit of land, not much. Jus' som'thin' that was his. Som'thin' he could live on and there couldn't nobody throw him off of it. I never had none. I planted crops for damn near ever'body in this state, but they wasn't my crops, and when I harvested 'em, it wasn't none of my harvest. But we gonna do it now, and don't you make no mistake about that. George ain't got the money in town. That money's in the bank. Me an' Lennie an' George. We gonna have a room to ourself. We're gonna have a dog an' rabbits an' chickens. We're gonna have green corn an' maybe a cow or a goat." He stopped, overwhelmed with his picture.

Crooks asked, "You say you got the money?"

---

3 **brutally** (adv.): brutal, gefühllos.

3 f. **to kid o.s.** (infml.): sich etwas vormachen.

28 **green corn:** frische Maiskolben.

"Damn right. We got most of it. Just a little bit more to get. Have it all in one month. George got the land all picked out, too."

Crooks reached around and explored his spine with his hand. "I never seen a guy really do it," he said. "I seen guys nearly crazy with loneliness for land, but ever'time a whore house or a blackjack game took what it takes." He hesitated. ". . . If you . . . guys would want a hand to work for nothing – just his keep, why I'd come an' lend a hand. I ain't so crippled I can't work like a son-of-a-bitch if I want to."

"Any you boys seen Curley?"

They swung their heads toward the door. Looking in was Curley's wife. Her face was heavily made up. Her lips were slightly parted. She breathed strongly, as though she had been running.

"Curley ain't been here," Candy said sourly.

She stood still in the doorway, smiling a little at them, rubbing the nails of one hand with the thumb and forefinger of the other. And her eyes traveled from one face to another. "They left all the weak ones here," she said finally. "Think I don't know where they all went? Even Curley. I know where they all went."

Lennie watched her, fascinated; but Candy and Crooks were scowling down away from her eyes. Candy said, "Then if you know, why you want to ast us where Curley is at?"

She regarded them amusedly. "Funny thing," she said.

---

7 **blackjack game:** Glücksspiel mit Karten (Siebzehn und Vier).

9 f. **to lend a hand:** sich nützlich machen, mit anpacken.

10 f. **like a son-of-a-bitch** (slang): emphatischer Vergleich; etwa: wie ein Gaul.

17 **sourly** (adv.): bitter.

"If I catch any one man, and he's alone, I get along fine with him. But just let two of the guys get together an' you won't talk. Jus' nothing but mad." She dropped her fingers and put her hands on her hips. "You're all scared of each other, that's what. Ever' one of you's scared the rest is goin' to get something on you."

After a pause Crooks said, "Maybe you better go along to your own house now. We don't want no trouble."

"Well, I ain't giving you no trouble. Think I don't like to talk to somebody ever' once in a while? Think I like to stick in that house alla time?"

Candy laid the stump of his wrist on his knee and rubbed it gently with his hand. He said accusingly, "You gotta husban'. You got no call foolin' aroun' with other guys, causin' trouble."

The girl flared up. "Sure I gotta husban'. You all seen him. Swell guy, ain't he? Spends all his time sayin' what he's gonna do to guys he don't like, and he don't like nobody. Think I'm gonna stay in that two-by-four house and listen how Curley's gonna lead with his left twicet, and then bring in the ol' right cross? 'One-two', he says. 'Jus' the ol' one-two an' he'll go down.'" She paused and her face lost its sullenness and grew interested. "Say – what happened to Curley's han'?"

1f. **to get along fine with s.o.:** prima mit jdm. auskommen.
6 **to get s.th. on s.o.** (slang): jdm. etwas anhängen.
17 **to flare up:** aufbrausen.
21 **to lead with one's left:** die Linke als Führhand einsetzen (Boxen).
    twicet (dial.): *twice:* hier: als Doublette geschlagen.
22 **the ol' right cross:** der gute alte rechte Haken (über die Auslage des Gegners geschlagen).
24 **sullenness:** Mißmutigkeit, Verdrießlichkeit.

There was an embarrassed silence. Candy stole a look
at Lennie. Then he coughed. "Why ... Curley ... he
got his han' caught in a machine, ma'am. Bust his
han'."

5 She watched for a moment, and then she laughed.
"Baloney! What you think you're sellin' me? Curley
started som'pin' he didn' finish. Caught in a machine –
baloney! Why, he ain't give nobody good ol' one-two
since he got his han' bust. Who bust him?"

10 Candy repeated sullenly, "Got it caught in a machine."

"Awright," she said contemptuously. "Awright, cover
'im up if ya wanta. Whatta I care? You bindle bums
think you're so damn good. Whatta ya think I am, a

15 kid? I tell ya I could of went with shows. Not jus' one,
neither. An' a guy tol' me he could put me in pitchers. ..." She was breathless with indignation. "– Sat'-
iday night. Ever'body out doin' som'pin'. Ever'body!
An' what am I doin'? Standin' here talkin' to a bunch of

20 bindle stiffs – a nigger an' a dum-dum and a lousy ol'
sheep – an' likin' it because they ain't nobody else."
Lennie watched her, his mouth half open. Crooks had
retired into the terrible protective dignity of the Negro.
But a change came over old Candy. He stood up

---

3 **ma'am** (infml.): *madam.*
6 **baloney** (slang): Blödsinn!
13 **bindle bum** (slang): (Gelegenheitsarbeit suchender) Landstreicher.
15 **show** (infml.): Tourneetheater.
16f. **in pitchers** (slang): *into the pictures:* zum Film, nach Hollywood.
17 **indignation:** Entrüstung.
20 **bindle stiff** (slang): wandernder Gelegenheitsarbeiter (meist Erntehelfer, der seine Habseligkeiten in einem *bindle* mit sich trägt).
dum-dum (slang): Idiot.
lousy (infml.): verlaust; (fig.) lausig.

suddenly and knocked his nail keg over backward. "I had enough," he said angrily. "You ain't wanted here. We told you you ain't. An' I tell ya, you got floozy idears about what us guys amounts to. You ain't got sense enough in that chicken head to even see that we ain't stiffs. S'pose you get us canned. S'pose you do. You think we'll hit the highway an' look for another lousy two-bit job like this. You don't know that we got our own ranch to go to, an' our own house. We ain't got to stay here. We gotta house and chickens an' fruit trees an' a place a hunderd time prettier than this. An' we got fren's, that's what we got. Maybe there was a time when we was scared of gettin' canned, but we ain't no more. We got our own lan', and it's ours, an' we c'n go to it."

Curley's wife laughed at him. "Baloney," she said. "I seen too many you guys. If you had two bits in the worl', why you'd be in gettin' two shots of corn with it and suckin' the bottom of the glass. I know you guys."

Candy's face had grown redder and redder, but before she was done speaking, he had control of himself. He was the master of the situation. "I might of knew," he said gently. "Maybe you just better go along an' roll your hoop. We ain't got nothing to say to you at all. We know what we got, and we don't care whether you know

---

3 **floozy** (slang): einfältig, dusselig.
7 **to hit the highway** (infml.): auf Achse gehen, sich trollen.
11 **time** (dial.): *times*.
14 **c'n** (dial.): *can*.
18 **corn** (AE): (billiger, illegal gebrannter) Whisky.
23 f. **to roll one's hoop** (infml.): wörtl.: seinen Reifen rollen; hier (fig.) etwa: spielen gehen und sich nicht in Sachen mischen, die man nicht versteht.

it or not. So maybe you better jus' scatter along now, 'cause Curley maybe ain't gonna like his wife out in the barn with us 'bindle stiffs'."

She looked from one face to another, and they were all closed against her. And she looked longest at Lennie, until he dropped his eyes in embarrassment. Suddenly she said, "Where'd you get them bruises on your face?"

Lennie looked up guiltily. "Who – me?"

"Yeah, you."

Lennie looked to Candy for help, and then he looked at his lap again. "He got his han' caught in a machine," he said.

Curley's wife laughed. "O. K., Machine. I'll talk to you later. I like machines."

Candy broke in. "You let this guy alone. Don't you do no messing aroun' with him. I'm gonna tell George what you says. George won't have you messin' with Lennie."

"Who's George?" she asked. "The little guy you come with?"

Lennie smiled happily. "That's him," he said. "That's the guy, an' he's gonna let me tend the rabbits."

"Well, if that's all you want, I might get a couple rabbits myself."

Crooks stood up from his bunk and faced her. "I had enough," he said coldly. "You got no rights comin' in a colored man's room. You got no rights messing around in here at all. Now you jus' get out, an' get out quick. If

---

1 **to scatter along** (slang): sich davonmachen, abschieben.
7 **bruise:** Bluterguß.

you don't, I'm gonna ast the boss not to ever let you come in the barn no more."

She turned on him in scorn. "Listen, Nigger," she said. "You know what I can do to you if you open your 5 trap?"

Crooks stared hopelessly at her, and then he sat down on his bunk and drew into himself.

She closed on him. "You know what I could do?"

Crooks seemed to grow smaller, and he pressed himself 10 against the wall. "Yes, ma'am."

"Well, you keep your place then, Nigger. I could get you strung up on a tree so easy it ain't even funny."

Crooks had reduced himself to nothing. There was no personality, no ego – nothing to arouse either like or 15 dislike. He said, "Yes, ma'am," and his voice was toneless.

For a moment she stood over him as though waiting for him to move so that she could whip at him again; but Crooks sat perfectly still, his eyes averted, everything 20 that might be hurt drawn in. She turned at last to the other two.

Old Candy was watching her, fascinated. "If you was to do that, we'd tell," he said quietly. "We'd tell about you framin' Crooks."

25 "Tell an' be damned," she cried. "Nobody'd listen to you, an' you know it. Nobody'd listen to you."

---

5 **trap** (slang): Klappe, Maul, Fresse.
11 f. **to get s.o. strung up** (infml.): jdn. an den Galgen bringen.
14 **ego:** Ego, Selbstbewußtsein.
19 **to avert one's eyes:** die Augen abwenden.
24 **to frame s.o.** (slang): jdm. (durch falsche Beschuldigungen) etwas ,anhängen'.

Candy subsided. "No . . ." he agreed. "Nobody'd listen to us."

Lennie whined, "I wisht George was here. I wisht George was here."

5 Candy stepped over to him. "Don't you worry none," he said. "I jus' heard the guys comin' in. George'll be in the bunkhouse right now, I bet." He turned to Curley's wife. "You better go home now," he said quietly. "If you go right now, we won't tell Curley you was 10 here."

She appraised him coolly. "I ain't sure you heard nothing."

"Better not take no chances," he said. "If you ain't sure, you better take the safe way."

15 She turned to Lennie. "I'm glad you bust up Curley a little bit. He got it comin' to him. Sometimes I'd like to bust him myself." She slipped out the door and disappeared into the dark barn. And while she went through the barn, the halter chains rattled, and some horses 20 snorted and some stamped their feet.

Crooks seemed to come slowly out of the layers of protection he had put on. "Was that the truth what you said about the guys come back?" he asked.

"Sure. I heard 'em."

25 "Well, I didn't hear nothing."

"The gate banged," Candy said, and he went on, "Jesus Christ, Curley's wife can move quiet. I guess she had a lot of practice, though."

Crooks avoided the whole subject now. "Maybe you 30 guys better go," he said. "I ain't sure I want you in here

---

11 **to appraise:** abschätzen, taxieren.
21 f. **layer of protection:** Schutzschicht.

no more. A colored man got to have some rights even if he don't like 'em."

Candy said, "That bitch didn't ought to of said that to you."

5 "It wasn't nothing," Crooks said dully. "You guys comin' in an' settin' made me forget. What she says is true."

The horses snorted out in the barn and the chains rang and a voice called, "Lennie. Oh, Lennie. You in the
10 barn?"

"It's George," Lennie cried. And he answered, "Here, George. I'm right in here."

In a second George stood framed in the door, and he looked disapprovingly about. "What you doin' in
15 Crooks' room? You hadn't ought to be here."

Crooks nodded. "I tol' 'em, but they come in anyways."

"Well, why'n't you kick 'em out?"

"I didn't care much," said Crooks. "Lennie's a nice
20 fella."

Now Candy aroused himself. "Oh, George! I been figurin' and figurin'. I got it doped out how we can even make some money on them rabbits."

George scowled. "I thought I tol' you not to tell nobody
25 about that."

Candy was crestfallen. "Didn't tell nobody but Crooks."

George said, "Well you guys get outa here. Jesus, seems like I can't go away for a minute."

---

18 **why'n't** (dial.): *why didn't.*
21 **to arouse o.s.:** lebendig werden, sich aufrappeln.
22 **to dope out** (slang): ausklügeln, ausbaldowern.
26 **crestfallen:** (fig.) geknickt.

Candy and Lennie stood up and went toward the door. Crooks called, "Candy!"

"Huh?"

"'Member what I said about hoein' and doin' odd
5 jobs?"

"Yeah," said Candy. "I remember."

"Well, jus' forget it," said Crooks. "I didn't mean it. Jus' foolin'. I wouldn' want to go no place like that."

10 "Well, O. K., if you feel like that. Good night."

The three men went out of the door. As they went through the barn the horses snorted and the halter chains rattled.

Crooks sat on his bunk and looked at the door for a
15 moment, and then he reached for the liniment bottle. He pulled out his shirt in back, poured a little liniment in his pink palm and, reaching around, he fell slowly to rubbing his back.

Five

20 One end of the great barn was piled high with new hay and over the pile hung the four-taloned Jackson fork suspended from its pulley. The hay came down like a mountain slope to the other end of the barn, and there was a level place as yet unfilled with the new crop. At

---

4 **'member** (infml.): *remember*.
21 **four-taloned:** vierzackig, mit vier Zinken.
   Jackson fork: mechanische Heuhebevorrichtung (wahrsch. nach dem Erfinder oder Hersteller benannt).
22 **to be suspended:** (frei) hängen.
   pulley: (Flaschenzug-)Rolle, Aufhängung.

the sides the feeding racks were visible, and between the slats the heads of horses could be seen.

It was Sunday afternoon. The resting horses nibbled the remaining wisps of hay, and they stamped their feet and they bit the wood of the mangers and rattled the halter chains. The afternoon sun sliced in through the cracks of the barn walls and lay in bright lines on the hay. There was the buzz of flies in the air, the lazy afternoon humming.

From outside came the clang of horseshoes on the playing peg and the shouts of men, playing, encouraging, jeering. But in the barn it was quiet and humming and lazy and warm.

Only Lennie was in the barn, and Lennie sat in the hay beside a packing case under a manger in the end of the barn that had not been filled with hay. Lennie sat in the hay and looked at a little dead puppy that lay in front of him. Lennie looked at it for a long time, and then he put out his huge hand and stroked it, stroked it clear from one end to the other.

And Lennie said softly to the puppy, "Why do you got to get killed? You ain't so little as mice. I didn't bounce you hard." He bent the pup's head up and looked in its face, and he said to it, "Now maybe George ain't gonna let me tend no rabbits, if he fin's out you got killed."

1 **feeding rack:** Futterkrippe.
2 **slat:** Latte.
4 **wisp:** Büschel.
5 **manger:** Futterkrippe.
6 **to slice in:** hier: in Streifen hereinfallen (Sonnenlicht).
12 **to jeer:** spötteln; buhen.
15 **packing case:** Kiste.
22 **to bounce:** hart schlagen.
25 **fin's** (dial.): *finds*.

He scooped a little hollow and laid the puppy in it and covered it over with hay, out of sight; but he continued to stare at the mound he had made. He said, "This ain't no bad thing like I got to go hide in the brush. Oh! no. This ain't. I'll tell George I foun' it dead."

He unburied the puppy and inspected it, and he stroked it from ears to tail. He went on sorrowfully, "But he'll know. George always knows. He'll say, 'You done it. Don't try to put nothing over on me.' An' he'll say, 'Now jus' for that you don't get to tend no rabbits!'"

Suddenly his anger arose. "God damn you," he cried. "Why do you got to get killed? You ain't so little as mice." He picked up the pup and hurled it from him. He turned his back on it. He sat bent over his knees and he whispered, "Now I won't get to tend the rabbits. Now he won't let me." He rocked himself back and forth in his sorrow.

From outside came the clang of horseshoes on the iron stake, and then a little chorus of cries. Lennie got up and brought the puppy back and laid it on the hay and sat down. He stroked the pup again. "You wasn't big enough," he said. "They tol' me and tol' me you wasn't. I di'n't know you'd get killed so easy." He worked his fingers on the pup's limp ear. "Maybe George won't care," he said. "This here God damn little son-of-a-bitch wasn't nothing to George."

Curley's wife came around the end of the last stall. She came very quietly, so that Lennie didn't see her. She wore her bright cotton dress and the mules with the red

3 **mound:** Haufen, Stoß.
25 **limp:** schlaff.

108

ostrich feathers. Her face was made up and the little sausage curls were all in place. She was quite near to him before Lennie looked up and saw her.

In a panic he shoveled hay over the puppy with his
5 fingers. He looked sullenly up at her.

She said, "What you got there, sonny boy?"

Lennie glared at her. "George says I ain't to have nothing to do with you – talk to you or nothing."

She laughed. "George giving you orders about every-
10 thing?"

Lennie looked down at the hay. "Says I can't tend no rabbits if I talk to you or anything."

She said quietly, "He's scared Curley'll get mad. Well, Curley got his arm in a sling – an' if Curley gets tough,
15 you can break his other han'. You didn't put nothing over on me about gettin' it caught in no machine."

But Lennie was not to be drawn. "No, sir. I ain't gonna talk to you or nothing."

She knelt in the hay beside him. "Listen," she said. "All
20 the guys got a horseshoe tenement goin' on. It's on'y about four o'clock. None of them guys is goin' to leave that tenement. Why can't I talk to you? I never get to talk to nobody. I get awful lonely."

Lennie said, "Well, I ain't supposed to talk to you or
25 nothing."

"I get lonely," she said. "You can talk to people, but I can't talk to nobody but Curley. Else he gets mad. How'd you like not to talk to anybody?"

---

5 **sullenly** (adv.): finster; mürrisch, verdrossen.
6 **sonny boy** (infml.): Kleiner, Sohnemann.
17 **to draw s.o.:** hier: jdn. vereinnahmen.
20 **tenement:** Gemeint ist *tournament:* Turnier, Wettkampf.

Lennie said, "Well, I ain't supposed to. George's scared I'll get in trouble."

She changed the subject. "What you got covered up there?"

5 Then all of Lennie's woe came back on him. "Jus' my pup," he said sadly. "Jus' my little pup." And he swept the hay from on top of it.

"Why, he's dead," she cried.

"He was so little," said Lennie. "I was jus' playin' with
10 him ... an' he made like he's gonna bite me ... an' I made like I was gonna smack him ... an' ... an' I done it. An' then he was dead."

She consoled him. "Don't you worry none. He was jus' a mutt. You can get another one easy. The whole
15 country is fulla mutts."

"It ain't that so much," Lennie explained miserably. "George ain't gonna let me tend no rabbits now."

"Why don't he?"

"Well, he said if I done any more bad things he ain't
20 gonna let me tend the rabbits."

She moved closer to him and she spoke soothingly. "Don't you worry about talkin' to me. Listen to the guys yell out there. They got four dollars bet in that tenement. None of them ain't gonna leave till it's over."

25 "If George sees me talkin' to you he'll give me hell," Lennie said cautiously. "He tol' me so."

Her face grew angry. "Wha's the matter with me?" she cried. "Ain't I got a right to talk to nobody? Whatta they think I am, anyways? You're a nice guy. I don't

---

11 **to smack:** schlagen.
14 **mutt** (slang): Hund, Promenadenmischung.
21 **soothingly** (adv.): beschwichtigend.

know why I can't talk to you. I ain't doin' no harm to you."

"Well, George says you'll get us in a mess."

"Aw, nuts!" she said. "What kinda harm am I doin' to
you? Seems like they ain't none of them cares how I
gotta live. I tell you I ain't used to livin' like this. I
coulda made somethin' of myself." She said darkly,
"Maybe I will yet." And then her words tumbled out in
a passion of communication, as though she hurried
before her listener could be taken away. "I lived right in
Salinas," she said. "Come there when I was a kid. Well,
a show come through, an' I met one of the actors. He
says I could go with that show. But my ol' lady wouldn't
let me. She says because I was on'y fifteen. But the guy
says I coulda. If I'd went, I wouldn't be livin' like this,
you bet."

Lennie stroked the pup back and forth. "We gonna
have a little place – an' rabbits," he explained.

She went on with her story quickly, before she should
be interrupted. "'Nother time I met a guy, an' he was in
pitchers. Went out to the Riverside Dance Palace with
him. He says he was gonna put me in the movies. Says I
was a natural. Soon's he got back to Hollywood he was
gonna write to me about it." She looked closely at
Lennie to see whether she was impressing him. "I never
got that letter," she said. "I always thought my ol' lady
stole it. Well, I wasn't gonna stay no place where I
couldn't get nowhere or make something of myself, an'
where they stole your letters, I ast her if she stole it, too,

---

5 **they ain't none of them cares** (dial.): *there isn't anybody who cares.*
23 **a natural** (infml.): *a natural talent.*
   soon's (dial.): *as soon as.*

an' she says no. So I married Curley. Met him out to the Riverside Dance Palace that same night." She demanded, "You listenin'?"

"Me? Sure."

5 "Well, I ain't told this to nobody before. Maybe I oughten to. I don' *like* Curley. He ain't a nice fella." And because she had confided in him, she moved closer to Lennie and sat beside him. "Coulda been in the movies, an' had nice clothes – all them nice clothes like
10 they wear. An' I coulda sat in them big hotels, an' had pitchers took of me. When they had them previews I coulda went to them, an' spoke in the radio, an' it wouldn'ta cost me a cent because I was in the pitcher. An' all them nice clothes like they wear. Because this
15 guy says I was a natural." She looked up at Lennie, and she made a small grand gesture with her arm and hand to show that she could act. The fingers trailed after her leading wrist, and her little finger stuck out grandly from the rest.

20 Lennie sighed deeply. From outside came the clang of a horseshoe on metal, and then a chorus of cheers. "Somebody made a ringer," said Curley's wife.

Now the light was lifting as the sun went down, and the sun streaks climbed up the wall and fell over the feeding
25 racks and over the heads of the horses.

Lennie said, "Maybe if I took this pup out and throwed him away George wouldn't never know. An' then I could tend the rabbits without no trouble."

---

6 **oughten** (dial.): *ought not.*
11 **preview:** Probeaufnahme.
22 **to make a ringer** (infml.): (beim Hufeisenwerfen) den Pflock treffen.
23 **the light was lifting:** das Licht wich nach oben zurück.

Curley's wife said angrily, "Don't you think of nothing but rabbits?"

"We gonna have a little place," Lennie explained patiently. "We gonna have a house an' a garden and a place for alfalfa, an' that alfalfa is for the rabbits, an' I take a sack and get it all fulla alfalfa and then I take it to the rabbits."

She asked, "What makes you so nuts about rabbits?"

Lennie had to think carefully before he could come to a conclusion. He moved cautiously close to her, until he was right against her. "I like to pet nice things. Once at a fair I seen some of them long-hair rabbits. An' they was nice, you bet. Sometimes I've even pet mice, but not when I couldn't get nothing better."

Curley's wife moved away from him a little. "I think you're nuts," she said.

"No I ain't," Lennie explained earnestly. "George says I ain't. I like to pet nice things with my fingers, sof' things."

She was a little bit reassured. "Well, who don't?" she said. "Ever'body likes that. I like to feel silk an' velvet. Do you like to feel velvet?"

Lennie chuckled with pleasure. "You bet, by God," he cried happily. "An' I had some, too. A lady give me some, an' that lady was – my own Aunt Clara. She give it right to me – 'bout this big a piece. I wisht I had that velvet right now." A frown came over his face. "I lost it," he said. "I ain't seen it for a long time."

Curley's wife laughed at him. "You're nuts," she said. "But you're a kinda nice fella. Jus' like a big baby. But a person can see kinda what you mean. When I'm doin' my hair sometimes I jus' set an' stroke it 'cause it's so

soft." To show how she did it, she ran her fingers over the top of her head. "Some people got kinda coarse hair," she said complacently. "Take Curley. His hair is jus' like wire. But mine is soft and fine. 'Course I brush
5 it a lot. That makes it fine. Here – feel right here." She took Lennie's hand and put it on her head. "Feel right aroun' there an' see how soft it is."

Lennie's big fingers fell to stroking her hair.

"Don't you muss it up," she said.

10 Lennie said, "Oh! That's nice," and he stroked harder. "Oh, that's nice."

"Look out, now, you'll muss it." And then she cried angrily, "You stop it now, you'll mess it all up." She jerked her head sideways, and Lennie's fingers closed
15 on her hair and hung on. "Let go," she cried. "You let go!"

Lennie was in a panic. His face was contorted. She screamed then, and Lennie's other hand closed over her mouth and nose. "Please don't," he begged. "Oh!
20 Please don't do that. George'll be mad."

She struggled violently under his hands. Her feet battered on the hay and she writhed to be free; and from under Lennie's hand came a muffled screaming. Lennie began to cry with fright. "Oh! Please don't do none of
25 that," he begged. "George gonna say I done a bad thing. He ain't gonna let me tend no rabbits." He moved his hand a little and her hoarse cry came out.

---

9 **to muss s.th. up** (slang): etwas in Unordnung bringen (*to muss: to mess*).

21f. **to batter:** heftig schlagen.

22 **to writhe:** sich winden.

23 **muffled:** gedämpft, unterdrückt.

27 **hoarse:** heiser.

Then Lennie grew angry. "Now don't," he said, "I don't want you to yell. You gonna get me in trouble jus' like George says you will. Now don't you do that." And she continued to struggle, and her eyes were wild with terror. He shook her then, and he was angry with her. "Don't you go yellin'," he said, and he shook her; and her body flopped like a fish. And then she was still, for Lennie had broken her neck.

He looked down at her, and carefully he removed his hand from over her mouth, and she lay still. "I don't want to hurt you," he said, "but George'll be mad if you yell." When she didn't answer nor move he bent closely over her. He lifted her arm and let it drop. For a moment he seemed bewildered. And then he whispered in fright, "I done a bad thing. I done another bad thing."

He pawed up the hay until it partly covered her.

From outside the barn came a cry of men and the double clang of shoes on metal. For the first time Lennie became conscious of the outside. He crouched down in the hay and listened. "I done a real bad thing," he said. "I shouldn't of did that. George'll be mad. An'... he said ... an' hide in the brush till he come. He's gonna be mad. In the brush till he come. Tha's what he said." Lennie went back and looked at the dead girl. The puppy lay close to her. Lennie picked it up. "I'll throw him away," he said. "It's bad enough like it is." He put the pup under his coat, and he crept to the barn wall and peered out between the cracks, toward

17 **to paw up:** aufhäufen (mit tapsigen Pfoten wie ein Bär).
22 **of did** (dial.): *have done.*

the horseshoe game. And then he crept around the end
of the last manger and disappeared.

The sun streaks were high on the wall by now, and the
light was growing soft in the barn. Curley's wife lay on
5 her back, and she was half covered with hay.

It was very quiet in the barn, and the quiet of the
afternoon was on the ranch. Even the clang of the
pitched shoes, even the voices of the men in the game,
seemed to grow more quiet. The air in the barn was
10 dusky in advance of the outside day. A pigeon flew in
through the open hay door and circled and flew out
again. Around the last stall came a shepherd bitch, lean
and long, with heavy, hanging dugs. Halfway to the
packing box where the puppies were she caught the
15 dead scent of Curley's wife, and the hair arose along her
spine. She whimpered and cringed to the packing box,
and jumped in among the puppies.

Curley's wife lay with a half-covering of yellow hay.
And the meanness and the plannings and the discontent
20 and the ache for attention were all gone from her face.
She was very pretty and simple, and her face was sweet
and young. Now her rouged checks and her reddened
lips made her seem alive and sleeping very lightly. The
curls, tiny little sausages, were spread on the hay behind
25 her head, and her lips were parted.

As happens sometimes, a moment settled and hovered
and remained for much more than a moment. And
sound stopped and movement stopped for much, much
more than a moment.

---

13 **dugs:** Zitzen.
16 **to cringe:** katzbuckeln, kriechen.
26 **to hover:** in der Schwebe bleiben.

Then gradually time awakened again and moved sluggishly on. The horses stamped on the other side of the feeding racks and the halter chains clinked. Outside, the men's voices became louder and clearer.

From around the end of the last stall old Candy's voice came. "Lennie," he called. "Oh, Lennie! You in here? I been figuring some more. Tell you what we can do, Lennie." Old Candy appeared around the end of the last stall. "Oh, Lennie!" he called again; and then he stopped, and his body stiffened. He rubbed his smooth wrist on his white stubble whiskers. "I di'n't know you was here," he said to Curley's wife.

When she didn't answer, he stepped nearer. "You oughten to sleep out here," he said disapprovingly; and then he was beside her and – "Oh, Jesus Christ!" He looked about helplessly, and he rubbed his beard. And then he jumped up und went quickly out of the barn.

But the barn was alive now. The horses stamped and snorted, and they chewed the straw of their bedding and they clashed the chains of their halters. In a moment Candy came back, and George was with him.

George said, "What was it you wanted to see me about?"

Candy pointed at Curley's wife. George stared. "What's the matter with her?" he asked. He stepped closer, and then he echoed Candy's words. "Oh, Jesus Christ!" He was down on his knees beside her. He put his hand over her heart. And finally, when he stood up, slowly and

---

1 f. **sluggishly** (adv.): träge.
20 **bedding:** Streu.
21 **to clash:** aneinanderschlagen.

stiffly, his face was as hard and tight as wood, and his eyes were hard.

Candy said, "What done it?"

George looked coldly at him. "Ain't you got any idear?" he asked. And Candy was silent. "I should of knew," George said hopelessly. "I guess maybe way back in my head I did."

Candy asked, "What we gonna do now, George? What we gonna do now?"

George was a long time in answering. "Guess ... we gotta tell the ... guys. I guess we gotta get 'im an' lock 'im up. We can't let 'im get away. Why, the poor bastard'd starve." And he tried to reassure himself. "Maybe they'll lock 'im up an' be nice to 'im."

But Candy said excitedly, "We oughta let 'im get away. You don't know that Curley. Curley gon'ta wanta get 'im lynched. Curley'll get 'im killed."

George watched Candy's lips. "Yeah," he said at last, "that's right, Curley will. An' the other guys will." And he looked back at Curley's wife.

Now Candy spoke his greatest fear. "You an' me can get that little place, can't we, George? You an' me can go there an' live nice, can't we, George? Can't we?"

Before George answered, Candy dropped his head and looked down at the hay. He knew.

George said softly, "– I think I knowed from the very first. I think I know'd we'd never do her. He usta like to hear about it so much I got to thinking maybe we would."

6f. **way back** (AE, infml.): weit hinten.
28 **usta** (dial.): *used to*.

118

"Then – it's all off?" Candy asked sulkily.

George didn't answer his question. George said, "I'll work my month an' I'll take my fifty bucks an' I'll stay all night in some lousy cat house. Or I'll set in some poolroom till ever'body goes home. An' then I'll come back an' work another month an' I'll have fifty bucks more."

Candy said, "He's such a nice fella. I didn' think he'd do nothing like this."

George still stared at Curley's wife. "Lennie never done it in meanness," he said. "All the time he done bad things, but he never done one of 'em mean." He straightened up and looked back at Candy. "Now listen. We gotta tell the guys. They got to bring him in, I guess. They ain't no way out. Maybe they won't hurt 'im." He said sharply, "I ain't gonna let 'em hurt Lennie. Now you listen. The guys might think I was in on it. I'm gonna go in the bunkhouse. Then in a minute you come out and tell the guys about her, and I'll come along and make like I never seen her. Will you do that? So the guys won't think I was in on it?"

Candy said, "Sure, George. Sure I'll do that."

"O.K. Give me a couple minutes then, and you come runnin' out an' tell like you jus' found her. I'm going now." George turned and went quickly out of the barn.

Old Candy watched him go. He looked helplessly back at Curley's wife, and gradually his sorrow and his anger

---

1 **off** (infml.): vorbei, (fig.) gestorben.
  sulkily (adv.): schmollend.
17 **to be in on s.th.** (infml.): in eine Sache verwickelt sein.
24 **to tell like** (dial.): *to talk as if.*

grew into words. "You God damn tramp," he said viciously. "You done it, di'n't you? I s'pose you're glad. Ever'body knowed you'd mess things up. You wasn't no good. You ain't no good now, you lousy tart." He sniveled, and his voice shook. "I could of hoed in the garden and washed dishes for them guys." He paused, and then went on in a singsong. And he repeated the old words: "If they was a circus or a baseball game . . . we would of went to her . . . jus' said 'ta hell with work,' an' went to her. Never ast nobody's say so. An' they'd of been a pig and chickens . . . an' in the winter . . . the little fat stove . . . an' the rain comin' . . . an' us jes' settin' there." His eyes blinded with tears and he turned and went weakly out of the barn, and he rubbed his bristly whiskers with his wrist stump.

Outside the noise of the game stopped. There was a rise of voices in question, a drum of running feet and the men burst into the barn. Slim and Carlson and young Whit and Curley, and Crooks keeping back out of attention range. Candy came after them, and last of all came George. George had put on his blue denim coat and buttoned it, and his black hat was pulled down low over his eyes. The men raced around the last stall. Their eyes found Curley's wife in the gloom, they stopped and stood still and looked.

Then Slim went quietly over to her, and he felt her wrist. One lean finger touched her cheek, and then his hand went under her slightly twisted neck and his

---

5 **to snivel:** heulen, flennen.

7 **singsong:** Singsang.

10 **say so** (infml.): Erlaubnis.

fingers explored her neck. When he stood up the men crowded near and the spell was broken.

Curley came suddenly to life. "I know who done it," he cried. "That big son-of-a-bitch done it. I know he done it. Why – ever'body else was out there playin' horse-shoes." He worked himself into a fury. "I'm gonna get him. I'm going for my shotgun. I'll kill the big son-of-a-bitch myself. I'll shoot 'im in the guts. Come on, you guys." He ran furiously out of the barn. Carlson said, "I'll get my Luger," and he ran out too.

Slim turned quietly to George. "I guess Lennie done it, all right," he said. "Her neck's bust. Lennie coulda did that."

George didn't answer, but he nodded slowly. His hat was so far down on his forehead that his eyes were covered.

Slim went on, "Maybe like that time in Weed you was tellin' about."

Again George nodded.

Slim sighed. "Well, I guess we got to get him. Where you think he might of went?"

It seemed to take George some time to free his words. "He – would of went south," he said. "We come from north so he would of went south."

"I guess we gotta get 'im," Slim repeated.

George stepped close. "Couldn' we maybe bring him in an' they'll lock him up? He's nuts, Slim. He never done this to be mean."

Slim nodded. "We might," he said. "If we could keep

---

2 **the spell was broken:** der Bann war gebrochen.
6 **to work o.s. into a fury:** sich in Rage versetzen, hineinsteigern.

Curley in, we might. But Curley's gonna want to shoot
'im. Curley's still mad about his hand. An' s'pose they
lock him up an' strap him down and put him in a cage.
That ain't no good, George."

5 "I know," said George, "I know."

Carlson came running in. "The bastard's stole my
Luger," he shouted. "It ain't in my bag." Curley followed him, and Curley carried a shotgun in his good
hand. Curley was cold now.

10 "All right, you guys," he said. "The nigger's got a
shotgun. You take it, Carlson. When you see 'um, don't
give 'im no chance. Shoot for his guts. That'll double
'im over."

Whit said excitedly, "I ain't got a gun."

15 Curley said, "You go in Soledad an' get a cop. Get Al
Wilts, he's deputy sheriff. Le's go now." He turned
suspiciously on George. "You're comin' with us,
fella."

"Yeah," said George. "I'll come. But listen, Curley.

20 The poor bastard's nuts. Don't shoot 'im. He di'n't
know what he was doin'."

"Don't shoot 'im?" Curley cried. "He got Carlson's
Luger. 'Course we'll shoot 'im."

George said weakly, "Maybe Carlson lost his gun."

25 "I seen it this morning," said Carlson. "No, it's been
took."

Slim stood looking down at Curley's wife. He said,
"Curley – maybe you better stay here with your wife."

---

3 **to strap s.o. down** (infml.): jdn. fesseln.
12f. **to double s.o. over:** jdn. über den Haufen werfen.
15 **cop** (slang): Polizist, ‚Bulle'.
16 **deputy sheriff:** Hilfssheriff.

Curley's face reddened. "I'm goin'," he said. "I'm gonna shoot the guts outa that big bastard myself, even if I only got one hand. I'm gonna get 'im."

Slim turned to Candy. "You stay here with her then, Candy. The rest of us better get goin'."

They moved away. George stopped a moment beside Candy and they both looked down at the dead girl until Curley called, "You George! You stick with us so we don't think you had nothin' to do with this."

George moved slowly after them, and his feet dragged heavily.

And when they were gone, Candy squatted down in the hay and watched the face of Curley's wife. "Poor bastard," he said softly.

The sound of the men grew fainter. The barn was darkening gradually and, in their stalls, the horses shifted their feet and rattled the halter chains. Old Candy lay down in the hay and covered his eyes with his arm.

Six

The deep green pool of the Salinas River was still in the late afternoon. Already the sun had left the valley to go climbing up the slopes of the Gabilan Mountains, and the hilltops were rosy in the sun. But by the pool among the mottled sycamores, a pleasant shade had fallen.

A water snake glided smoothly up the pool, twisting its periscope head from side to side; and it swam the length

---

12 **to squat:** hocken.
26 **smoothly** (adv.): geschmeidig, elegant.

of the pool and came to the legs of a motionless heron
that stood in the shallows. A silent head and beak
lanced down and plucked it out by the head, and the
beak swallowed the little snake while its tail waved
5 frantically.

A far rush of wind sounded and a gust drove through
the tops of the trees like a wave. The sycamore leaves
turned up their silver sides, the brown, dry leaves on the
ground scudded a few feet. And row on row of tiny wind
10 waves flowed up the pool's green surface.

As quickly as it had come, the wind died, and the
clearing was quiet again. The heron stood in the shallows, motionless and waiting. Another little water
snake swam up the pool, turning its periscope head
15 from side to side.

Suddenly Lennie appeared out of the brush, and he
came as silently as a creeping bear moves. The heron
pounded the air with its wings, jacked itself clear of the
water and flew off down river. The little snake slid in
20 among the reeds at the pool's side.

Lennie came quietly to the pool's edge. He knelt down
and drank, barely touching his lips to the water. When a
little bird skittered over the dry leaves behind him, his
head jerked up and he strained toward the sound with
25 eyes and ears until he saw the bird, and then he dropped
his head and drank again.

---

2 **shallow:** seichte Stelle.
3 **to lance down:** wie eine Lanze herunterstoßen.
5 **frantically** (adv.): wild verzweifelt.
6 **gust:** Windstoß, Bö.
9 **to scud:** hier: (vom Wind getrieben) über den Boden fegen.
18 **to jack o.s. clear** (infml.): hier: sich kraftvoll in die Luft erheben.
23 **to skitter:** huschen, trippeln.

When he was finished, he sat down on the bank, with his side to the pool, so that he could watch the trail's entrance. He embraced his knees and laid his chin down on his knees.

The light climbed on out of the valley, and as it went, the tops of the mountains seemed to blaze with increasing brightness.

Lennie said softly, "I di'n't forget, you bet. God damn. Hide in the brush an' wait for George." He pulled his hat down low over his eyes. "George gonna give me hell," he said. "George gonna wish he was alone an' not have me botherin' him." He turned his head and looked at the bright mountain tops. "I can go right off there an' find a cave," he said. And he countinued sadly, "– an' never have no ketchup – but I won't care. If George don't want me . . . I'll go away. I'll go away."

And then from out of Lennie's head there came a little fat old woman. She wore thick bull's-eye glasses and she wore a huge gingham apron with pockets, and she was starched and clean. She stood in front of Lennie and put her hands on her hips, and she frowned disapprovingly at him.

And when she spoke, it was in Lennie's voice. "I tol' you an' tol' you," she said. "I tol' you, 'Min' George because he's such a nice fella an' good to you.' But you don't never take no care. You do bad things."

---

2 **trail:** Pfad.
18 **bull's-eye glasses** (infml., pl.): Bifokalbrille mit runden, stärkeren Linsen in der Mitte der Gläser (*bull's eye:* Schwarzes einer Zielscheibe).
19 **gingham:** Gingam, karierter Baumwollstoff.
20 **starched:** gestärkt (Stoff).
24 **to mind s.o.:** auf jdn. hören.

And Lennie answered her, "I tried, Aunt Clara, ma'am.
I tried and tried. I couldn't help it."

"You never give a thought to George," she went on in
Lennie's voice. "He been doin' nice things for you alla
5 time. When he got a piece of pie you always got half or
more'n half. An' if they was any ketchup, why he'd give
it all to you."

"I know," said Lennie miserably. "I tried, Aunt Clara,
ma'am. I tried and tried."

10 She interrupted him. "All the time he coulda had such a
good time if it wasn't for you. He woulda took his pay
an' raised hell in a whore house, and he coulda set in a
pool room an' played snooker. But he got to take care
of you."

15 Lennie moaned with grief. "I know, Aunt Clara,
ma'am. I'll go right off in the hills an' I'll fin' a cave
an' I'll live there so I won't be no more trouble to
George."

"You jus' say that," she said sharply. "You're always
20 sayin' that, an' you know sonofabitching well you ain't
never gonna do it. You'll jus' stick around an' stew the
b'Jesus outa George all the time."

Lennie said, "I might jus' as well go away. George ain't
gonna let me tend no rabbits now."

25 Aunt Clara was gone, and from out of Lennie's head
there came a gigantic rabbit. It sat on its haunches in

---

13 **snooker:** Billardvariante, bei der verschiedenfarbige Bälle in be-
stimmter Reihenfolge versenkt werden müssen.
20 **sonofabitching well** (slang): verdammt gut.
21f. **to stew the b'Jesus out of s.o.** (slang): jdm. unsäglich auf die
Nerven fallen.
26 **haunches:** Hinterläufe.

front of him, and it waggled its ears and crinkled its nose at him. And it spoke in Lennie's voice too.

"Tend rabbits," it said scornfully. "You crazy bastard. You ain't fit to lick the boots of no rabbit. You'd forget 'em and let 'em go hungry. That's what you'd do. An' then what would George think?"

"I would *not* forget," Lennie said loudly.

"The hell you wouldn'," said the rabbit. "You ain't worth a greased jack-pin to ram you into hell. Christ knows George done ever'thing he could to jack you outa the sewer, but it don't do no good. If you think George gonna let you tend rabbits, you're even crazier'n usual. He ain't. He's gonna beat hell outa you with a stick, that's what he's gonna do."

Now Lennie retorted belligerently, "He ain't neither. George won't do nothing like that. I've knew George since – I forget when – and he ain't never raised his han' to me with a stick. He's nice to me. He ain't gonna be mean."

"Well, he's sick of you," said the rabbit. "He's gonna beat hell outa you an' then go away an' leave you."

"He won't," Lennie cried frantically. "He won't do nothing like that. I know George. Me an' him travels together."

---

1 **to waggle:** wackeln.
   to crinkle one's nose: die Nase hochziehen, rümpfen.
8f. **You ain't worth a greased jack-pin to ram you into hell:** etwa: Du bist nicht den geölten Bolzen wert, der dich in die Hölle rammt (*greased:* geölt, geschmiert; *jack-pin:* nicht näher bestimmbares zylindrisches Maschinenteil).
11 **sewer:** Kloake.
15 **to retort:** scharf erwidern.
   belligerently (adv.): kampflustig, aggressiv.

But the rabbit repeated softly over and over, "He gonna leave you, ya crazy bastard. He gonna leave ya all alone. He gonna leave ya, crazy bastard."

Lennie put his hands over his ears. "He ain't, I tell ya
5 he ain't." And he cried, "Oh! George – George – George!"

George came quietly out of the brush and the rabbit scuttled back into Lennie's brain.

George said quietly, "What the hell you yellin'
10 about?"

Lennie got up on his knees. "You ain't gonna leave me, are ya, George? I know you ain't."

George came stiffly near and sat down beside him. "No."

15 "I knowed it," Lennie cried. "You ain't that kind."

George was silent.

Lennie said, "George."

"Yeah?"

"I done another bad thing."

20 "It don't make no difference," George said, and he fell silent again.

Only the topmost ridges were in the sun now. The shadow in the valley was blue and soft. From the distance came the sound of men shouting to one
25 another. George turned his head and listened to the shouts.

Lennie said, "George."

"Yeah?"

---

8 **to scuttle:** hoppeln.
22 **topmost:** oberst, höchst.
  ridge: (Berg-)Kamm, Grat.

128

"Ain't you gonna give me hell?"

"Give ya hell?"

"Sure, like you always done before. Like, 'If I di'n't have you I'd take my fifty bucks —'"

"Jesus Christ, Lennie! You can't remember nothing that happens, but you remember ever' word I say."

"Well, ain't you gonna say it?"

George shook himself. He said woodenly, "If I was alone I could live so easy." His voice was monotonous, had no emphasis. "I could get a job an' not have no mess." He stopped.

"Go on," said Lennie. "An' when the enda the month come —"

"An' when the end of the month came I could take my fifty bucks an' go to a ... cat house ..." He stopped again.

Lennie looked eagerly at him. "Go on, George. Ain't you gonna give me no more hell?"

"No," said George.

"Well, I can go away," said Lennie. "I'll go right off in the hills an' find a cave if you don' want me."

George shook himself again. "No," he said. "I want you to stay with me here."

Lennie said craftily – "Tell me like you done before."

"Tell you what?"

"'Bout the other guys an' about us."

George said, "Guys like us got no fambly. They make a little stake an' then they blow it in. They ain't got

9 **monotonous:** monoton, eintönig.
10 **emphasis:** Nachdruck.

nobody in the worl' that gives a hoot in hell about
'em —"

"But not us," Lennie cried happily. "Tell about us
now."

5 George was quiet for a moment. "But not us," he
said.

"Because —"

"Because I got you an'—"

"An' I got you. We got each other, that's what, that
10 gives a hoot in hell about us," Lennie cried in tri-
umph.

The little evening breeze blew over the clearing and the
leaves rustled and the wind waves flowed up the green
pool. And the shouts of men sounded again, this time
15 much closer than before.

George took off his hat. He said shakily, "Take off your
hat, Lennie. The air feels fine."

Lennie removed his hat dutifully and laid it on the
ground in front of him. The shadow in the valley was
20 bluer, and the evening came fast. On the wind the
sound of crashing in the brush came to them.

Lennie said, "Tell how it's gonna be."

George had been listening to the distant sounds. For a
moment he was businesslike. "Look acrost the river,
25 Lennie, an' I'll tell you so you can almost see it."

Lennie turned his head and looked off across the pool
and up the darkening slopes of the Gabilans. "We
gonna get a little place," George began. He reached in

---

1 f. *(not)* **to give a hoot in hell about s.o.** (slang): sich einen Dreck um
jdn. scheren.
21 **sound of crashing:** Geräusch knackender Äste.
24 **businesslike:** sachlich, nüchtern.

his side pocket and brought out Carlson's Luger; he snapped off the safety, and the hand and gun lay on the ground behind Lennie's back. He looked at the back of Lennie's head, at the place where the spine and skull were joined.

A man's voice called from up the river, and another man answered.

"Go on," said Lennie.

George raised the gun and his hand shook, and he dropped his hand to the ground again.

"Go on," said Lennie. "How's it gonna be. We gonna get a little place."

"We'll have a cow," said George. "An' we'll have maybe a pig an' chickens . . . an' down the flat we'll have a . . . little piece alfalfa —"

"For the rabbits," Lennie shouted.

"For the rabbits," George repeated.

"And I get to tend the rabbits."

"An' you get to tend the rabbits."

Lennie giggled with happiness. "An' live on the fatta the lan'."

"Yes."

Lennie turned his head.

"No, Lennie. Look down there acrost the river, like you can almost see the place."

Lennie obeyed him. George looked down at the gun.

There were crashing footsteps in the brush now. George turned and looked toward them.

"Go on, George. When we gonna do it?"

"Gonna do it soon."

---

2 **to snap off the safety:** (Waffe) entsichern.

"Me an' you."

"You . . . an' me. Ever'body gonna be nice to you. Ain't gonna be no more trouble. Nobody gonna hurt nobody nor steal from 'em."

5 Lennie said, "I thought you was mad at me, George."

"No," said George. "No, Lennie. I ain't mad. I never been mad, an' I ain't now. That's a thing I want ya to know."

10 The voices came close now. George raised the gun and listened to the voices.

Lennie begged, "Le's do it now. Le's get that place now."

"Sure, right now. I gotta. We gotta."

15 And George raised the gun and steadied it, and he brought the muzzle of it close to the back of Lennie's head. The hand shook violently, but his face set and his hand steadied. He pulled the trigger. The crash of the shot rolled up the hills and rolled down again. Lennie

20 jarred, and then settled slowly forward to the sand, and he lay without quivering.

George shivered and looked at the gun, and then he threw it from him, back up on the bank, near the pile of old ashes.

25 The brush seemed filled with cries and with the sound of running feet. Slim's voice shouted. "George. Where you at, George?"

But George sat stiffly on the bank and looked at his right hand that had thrown the gun away. The group

30 burst into the clearing, and Curley was ahead. He saw

---

16 **muzzle:** Mündung (einer Schußwaffe).
20 **to jar:** erstarren.

Lennie lying on the sand. "Got him, by God." He went over and looked down at Lennie, and then he looked back at George. "Right in the back of the head," he said softly.

5 Slim came directly to George and sat down beside him, sat very close to him. "Never you mind," said Slim. "A guy got to sometimes."

But Carlson was standing over George. "How'd you do it?" he asked.

10 "I just done it," George said tiredly.

"Did he have my gun?"

"Yeah. He had your gun."

"An' you got it away from him and you took it an' you killed him?"

15 "Yeah. Tha's how." George's voice was almost a whisper. He looked steadily at his right hand that had held the gun.

Slim twitched George's elbow. "Come on, George. Me an' you'll go in an' get a drink."

20 George let himself be helped to his feet. "Yeah, a drink."

Slim said, "You hadda, George. I swear you hadda. Come on with me." He led George into the entrance of the trail and up toward the highway.

25 Curley and Carlson looked after them. And Carlson said, "Now what the hell ya suppose is eatin' them two guys?"

---

18 **to twitch:** zupfen.
26f. **What ... is eatin' them two guys?** (slang): Was ... die zwei bloß haben?

Editorische Notiz

Der englische Text folgt der Ausgabe: *The Short Novels of John Steinbeck*, New York: The Viking Press, [7]1972, S. 203 bis 272. Das Glossar erklärt in der Regel alle Wörter, die über die Wertigkeitsstufe 4 des *Englischen Arbeitswörterbuches* von Alfred Haase (Frankfurt a. M.: Moritz Diesterweg, [7]1979) hinausgehen. Im Zweifelsfall wurde großzügig verfahren, d. h. eher eine Vokabel mehr aufgenommen als dort vorgesehen.

Bei der Angabe der Stilebenen bedeutet »slang« durchgehend amerikanischer Slang; bei der Zuordnung zum umgangssprachlichen Gebrauch werden spezifisch amerikanische Wendungen als solche gekennzeichnet. Es muß allerdings darauf hingewiesen werden, daß in Einzelfällen diese Unterscheidungen äußerst problematisch sein können.[1] Bei den meisten im Glossar angegebenen phonologischen und morphologischen Eigenheiten der Dialoge wurde die Bezeichnung »dialectal« der Zuordnung »slang« vorgezogen, da gerade im Amerikanischen die sozial übergreifende Verbreitung solcher sprachlicher Merkmale eine Einordnung unter Slang ad absurdum führen würde. Unter dieser Prämisse sind auch viele der folgenden Abweichungen von der Standardsprache zu beurteilen, die wegen ihrer Häufigkeit nur dann im Glossar kommentiert werden, wenn sie Verständnisschwierigkeiten bereiten:

I. Phonologische Eigenheiten

1. *Über das grammatikalisch abgegrenzte Maß hinausgehende Kontraktionen*

gonna/gon'ta: going to
whatta I got: what have I got

---

1 Einerseits ist im Amerikanischen die Grenze zwischen Umgangssprache und Slang fließend, andererseits nimmt im Englischen in den letzten Jahrzehnten der Einfluß von Amerikanismen (nicht zuletzt durch das Angebot an US-Filmen) drastisch zu, so daß vor allem in letzterem Fall eine Unterscheidung eher auf die Entstehungszeit des Textes als auf die heutige Sprachlandschaft zu beziehen ist.

Why'n't you do it yourself: Why don't you do it yourself
How'd you like the boss: How did you like the boss
alla time: all of the time
wanna: want to
George wun't go away: G. wouldn't go away
My brothers'd set on a fence rail: My brothers would set on a
  fence rail.
I do' know / I dunno: I don't know
Whatta I care: What do I care
di'n't you: didn't you

2. *Auslassung von Verschlußlauten am Wortende*

le's see: let's see
an': and
goin': going
jus'/jes': just
slep': slept
I tol' him: I told him
lef' somethin': left something
las' Sat'day: last Saturday
he fin's out: he finds out
Wha's the matter: What's the matter
I oughten to: I oughtn't to
sof': soft
min' George: mind George

3. *Auslassung von Vokalen und Liquiden im Wort- oder Phra-
   seninneren nach /n/ oder /r/*

ever' job: every job
on'y: only
soon's : as soon as

4. *Auslassung von /h/ und /th/ am Wortanfang in unbetonter
   Stellung*

You could just as well of rode: You could just as well have
  ridden (vgl. II.2)
then you forget 'em: then you forget them

I musta lost it: I must have lost it (vgl. I.1)
I had 'im ever since: I had him ever since
most of 'em: most of them
give 'um to me: give them/him to me
cover 'im up: cover him up

5. *Auslassung des Präfixes bzw. des ersten Gliedes in zweisilbigen bzw. -gliedrigen Adjektiven oder Adverbien*

'bout half an hour ago: about half an hour ago
'stead of doing all the work: instead of doing all the work
'course: of course

6. */a/ als Schwachstufe von »of« und »to« in unbetonter Stellung bzw. von /-ow/ am Wortende*

(Vgl. auch Kontraktionen, I.1)

kinda scummy: kind of scummy
outa that pocket: out of that pocket
I forget some a' the things: I forget some of the things
you never oughta: you never ought to
didn't wanta stop: didn't want to stop
I gotta tell you: I (have) got to tell you
tomorra: tomorrow
fella: fellow

7. *Kurzformen von Präpositionen nach dem Muster der Hilfsverben*

cockier'n ever: cockier than ever
wait'll you see: wait until you see

II. Morphologische Besonderheiten

1. *Gebrauch von »ain't« statt der Formen von »to be not« und »to have not«*

I ain't sure: I am not sure
I ain't got mine: I haven't got mine

136

they ain't none of them cares: there isn't anybody who cares
(vgl. II.3, III.6 und III.7)

2. *Gebrauch grammatikalisch falscher Verbformen*

I wisht: I wished
brang: brought
when he's spoke to: when he is spoken to
I've knew him for a long time: I've known him for a long
time
I would of had to drowned most of 'em: I would have to drown
most of them
I knowed: I knew
before I ever eat them: before I ever ate them
you might of saw her: you might have seen her
I coulda went: I could have gone
I shouldn't of did that: I shouldn't have done that
The bastard's stole my Luger: The bastard has stolen my Luger
it's been took: it has been taken

3. *Gebrauch von »them« statt »that« oder »those« bzw. »they« statt »there«*

All you ever can remember is them rabbits: All you ever can
remember are those rabbits
them God damn turnips: those God damn turnips
none of them guys: none of those guys
I seen 'em poison: I've seen that (kind of) poison
they ain't none of them cares: there isn't anybody who cares
An' they'd of been a pig and chickens: And there would have
been a pig and chickens

III. Syntaktische Besonderheiten

1. *Auslassung des Subjekts*

don't really seem: it doesn't really seem (vgl. III.4)
didn't wanta stop: he didn't want to stop

2. *Auslassung der Hilfsverben*

you gonna be sick: you are going to be sick
look what I done: look what I have done
What ya want?: What do you want?
Where we goin'?: Where are we going?
Ya got that?: Have you got that?
I jus' come here: I have just come here (vgl. III.3)
You God damn right: You are God damn right
George giving you orders?: Is George giving you orders?

3. *Gebrauch des Präsens statt anderer Tempora*

The white kids come to play: The white kids came to play
the little guy you come with: the little guy you came with
She give it right to me: She gave it right to me

4. *Fehlende Kongruenz in Numerus oder Person zwischen Subjekt und Prädikat*

don't really seem: it doesn't really seem (vgl. III.1)
if you was thirsty: if you were thirsty
you says: you say
they was looking for us: they were looking for us
we was gonna have fun: we were going to have fun
it don't take no figuring: it doesn't take any figuring (vgl. III.7)
I comes running: I came running (vgl. II.2 und III.3)

5. *Gebrauch des Hauptsatzes als Präpositionalobjekt*

on account of the nigger's got a crooked back: on account of
  the fact that the nigger has got a crooked back

6. *Gebrauch von Ellipsen*

wonder he isn't: it's a wonder he isn't
Seen my old man? Have you seen my old man?
There's plenty done that: There's plenty who have done that
Ain't many guys who travel: There aren't many guys who
  travel

He's the guy wrote the letter: He's the guy who wrote the letter
any you guys: any of you guys

7. *Doppelte Verneinung*

it didn't do no good: it didn't do any good
I didn't hear nothing: I didn't hear anything
don't never listen: don't ever listen
don't you worry none: don't worry

8. *Auslassung des unbestimmten Artikels*

Guy don't need no sense: A guy doesn't need any sense (vgl.
 III.4 und III.7)
ranch with a bunch of guys on it: a ranch with a bunch of guys
 on it

Im Glossar verwendete Abkürzungen

adv.	adverb
AE	American English
dial.	dialectal (mundartlich)
fig.	figuratively (übertragen)
infml.	informal (umgangssprachlich)
o.s.	oneself
pl.	plural
s.o.	someone
span.	spanisch
s.th.	something
vulg.	vulgar (vulgär, derb)

Anmerkung zum Titel

Der Titel ist der siebten Strophe des Gedichts »To a Mouse, on Turning her up in her Nest, with the Plough, November 1785« von Robert Burns (1759–96) entnommen. Da *Of Mice and Men* nicht der ursprünglich von Steinbeck vorgesehene Titel war, ist es nicht sinnvoll anzunehmen, sein Kurzroman gehe von dem Gedicht aus; trotzdem läßt die nachträgliche Änderung darauf schließen, daß Steinbeck sich einer grundsätzli-

To a Mouse, on Turning her up in her Nest, with the Plough, November 1785

Wee, sleekit, cowran, tim'rous beastie,
O, what a panic's in thy breastie!
Thou need na start awa sae hasty
   Wi' bickering brattle!
I wad be laith to rin an' chase thee,
   Wi' murdering pattle!

I'm truly sorry man's dominion
Has broken Nature's social union,
An' justifies that ill opinion
   Which makes thee startle
At me, thy poor, earth-born companion
   An' fellow mortal!

I doubt na, whyles, but thou may thieve:
What then? poor beastie, thou maun live!
A daimen icker in a thrave
   'S a sma' request;
I'll get a blessin wi' the lave,
   An' never miss't!

chen Affinität bewußt war. Um einen Vergleich der in beiden Werken vorzufindenden Identifikation von tierischem und menschlichem Bereich zu ermöglichen, sei das Gedicht des schottischen Romantikers hier in voller Länge wiedergegeben (zit. nach: *The Selected Poems of Robert Burns*, hrsg. von David Daiches, London 1979, S. 65 f.; die beigefügte Prosaübertragung erhebt in keiner Weise den Anspruch, der poetischen Qualität der Vorlage gerecht zu werden, sie soll lediglich den inhaltlichen Nachvollzug des Textes erleichtern).

Auf eine Maus, als er sie mit ihrem Nest umpflügte, im November 1785

Kleines, geschmeidiges, kauerndes, ängstliches Tierchen, / o welch panische Angst sitzt Dir in der Brust! / Du mußt nicht so hastig und aufgeschreckt / mit zänkischem Quietschen davonhuschen! / Es wäre mir ein Graus, Dir nachzulaufen, Dich zu jagen / mit dem todbringenden Pflugholz.

Es stimmt mich wahrhaft traurig, daß des Menschen Herrschaft / das soziale Gefüge der Natur zerbrochen hat / und die irrige Meinung rechtfertigt, / die Dich erschrecken läßt / vor mir, Deinem armen, irdischen Gefährten / und sterblichen Leidensgenossen!

Ich zweifle nicht daran, daß Du manchmal stiehlst: / Na und? armes Vieh, auch Du mußt leben! / Hier mal 'ne Ähre und dort aus 'nem Scheffel / ist nicht zuviel verlangt. / Ich bin genügend gut bedacht mit dem, was übrig ist, / und vermisse nie, was fehlt!

Thy wee-bit housie, too, in ruin!
Its silly wa's the win's are strewin!
An' naething, now, to big a new ane,
            O' foggage green!
An' bleak December's win's ensuin,
            Baith snell an' keen!

Thou saw the fields laid bare an' waste,
An' weary winter comin fast,
An' cozie' here, beneath the blast,
            Thou thought to dwell,
Till crash! the cruel coulter past
            Out thro' thy cell.

That wee-bit heap o' leaves an' stibble,
Has cost thee monie a weary nibble!
Now thou's turned out, for a' thy trouble,
            But house or hald,
To thole the winter's sleety dribble,
            An' cranreuch cauld!

But Mousie, thou art no thy lane,
In proving foresight may be vain:
The best-laid schemes o' mice an' men
            Gang aft agley,
An' lea'e us nought but grief an' pain,
            For promis'd joy!

Still, thou art blest, compared wi' me!
The present only toucheth thee:
But och! I backward cast my e'e,
            On prospects drear!
An' forward, tho' I canna see,
            I guess an' fear!

Deine winzige Wohnung nun auch in Trümmern! / Ihre zerbrechlichen Wände zerstreuen die Winde! / Und nichts hast Du nun, eine neue zu bauen / aus grünem Moos! / Und die rauhen Dezemberwinde stehen bevor, / stürmisch und schneidend!

Du sahst die Felder kahl und wüst werden, / und den trüben Winter schnell heranziehen / und dachtest, gemütlich hier unter dem Sturm / zu hausen, / bis krach! die grausame Pflugschar von draußen / durch Deine Kammer fuhr.

Dieser winzige Haufen von Blättern und Stoppeln / hat Dich manch mühsames Nagen gekostet! / Nun bist Du heimatlos, trotz all Deiner Mühen, / ohne Haus noch Grund, / ausgesetzt dem Schneeregen des Winters / und seinem kalten Rauhreif!

Doch, Mäuslein, Du stehst nicht allein, / wenn Dein Beispiel belegt, daß auch die klügste Vorsorge vergeblich sein kann: / Die noch so gut ausgedachten Pläne von Mäusen und Menschen / nehmen oft eine ganz andere Richtung / und lassen uns nichts außer Kummer und Schmerz / statt des versprochenen Glücks!

Dennoch bist Du, verglichen mit mir, glücklich zu schätzen! / Dich berührt nur der Augenblick: / Doch, ach! Mein Blick fällt auch zurück / auf trübe Bilder! / Und nach vorn, wiewohl der Blick mir verwehrt ist, / bleibt mir nur ängstliches Vermuten!

Literaturhinweise

I. *Werke*

Cup of Gold, New York, 1929; dt. *Eine Handvoll Gold*, 1953.

The Pastures of Heaven, New York, 1932; dt. *Das Tal des Himmels*, 1954.

To a God Unknown, New York, 1933; dt. *Der fremde Gott*, 1954.

Tortilla Flat, New York, 1935; dt. *Die wunderlichen Schelme von Tortilla Flat*, 1943.

In Dubious Battle, New York, 1936; dt. *Stürmische Ernte*, 1955.

Of Mice and Men, New York, 1937; dt. *Von Mäusen und Menschen*, 1947.

The Long Valley, New York, 1938.

The Grapes of Wrath, New York, 1939; dt. *Früchte des Zorns*, 1940.

Sea of Cortez. A Leisurely Journal of Travel and Research, New York, 1941; dt. *Logbuch des Lebens*, 1963.

Bombs Away. The Story of a Bomber Team, New York, 1942.

The Moon is Down, New York, 1942; dt. *Der Mond ging unter*, 1943.

Cannery Row, New York, ersch. 1944, dat. 1945; dt. *Die Straße der Ölsardinen*, 1946.

The Red Pony, New York, 1945; dt. *Der rote Pony*, 1945.

The Wayward Bus, New York, 1947; dt. *Autobus auf Seitenwegen*, 1948.

The Pearl, New York, 1947; dt. *Die Perle*, 1949.

A Russian Journal, New York, 1948.

Burning Bright, New York, 1950; dt. *Die wilde Flamme*, 1952.

East of Eden, New York, 1952; dt. *Jenseits von Eden*, 1953.

Sweet Thursday, New York, 1954; dt. *Wonniger Donnerstag*, 1955.

The Short Reign of Pippin IV: A Fabrication, New York, 1957; dt. *Laßt uns König spielen*, 1958.

Once There Was a War, New York, 1958.

The Winter of Our Discontent, New York, 1961; dt. *Geld bringt Geld*, 1962.

Travels with Charley in Search of America, New York, 1962; dt. *Meine Reise mit Charley*, 1963.

America and the Americans, New York, 1966; dt. *Amerika und die Amerikaner*, 1966.

Journal of a Novel, New York, 1969; dt. *Tagebuch eines Romans*, 1970.

II. *Bibliographien*

Beebe, Maurice / Bryer, J. R., »Criticism of John Steinbeck: A Selected Checklist«, in: *Modern Fiction Studies* 11 (1965) S. 90–103.

Hayashi, Tetsumaro, *John Steinbeck: A Concise Bibliography (1930–65)*, Metuchen (N. J.) 1967.

– *A New Steinbeck Bibliography (1929–1971)*, Metuchen (N. J.) 1973.

– *A New Steinbeck Bibliography (1971–1981)*, Metuchen (N. J.) 1983. Fortgef. von Meyer (1989) [s. u.].

Harmon, Robert B., *The First Editions of John Steinbeck*, Los Altos (Cal.) 1978.

Meyer, Michael J., *The Hayashi Bibliography, 1982–1996*, Lanham, Md. 1998.

III. *Zeitschrift*

Steinbeck Newsletter 1 (1968); ab Bd. 2 (1969) u. d. T. *Steinbeck Quarterly*, hrsg. von Tetsumaro Hayashi.

IV. *Biographien*

Benson, Jackson J., *The True Adventures of John Steinbeck, Writer*, New York, 1984.

145

Kiernan, Thomas, *The Intricate Music. A Biography of John Steinbeck*, Boston 1979.

Lisca, Peter, »John Steinbeck: A Literary Biography«, in: Tedlock, E. W. jr. / Wicker, C. V. (Hrsg.), *Steinbeck and his Critics*, Albuquerque 1957.

Moore, Harry T., »A Biographical Sketch«, in: H. T. M., *The Novels of John Steinbeck*, Chicago 1939, S. 73–90.

Parini, Jay, *John Steinbeck: A Biography*, New York 1995.

Steinbeck, Elaine / Wallsten, Robert (Hrsg.), *Steinbeck: A Life in Letters*, New York 1975.

St. Pierre, Brian, *John Steinbeck: The Californian Years*, San Francisco 1983.

Valjean, Nelson, *John Steinbeck: The Errant Knight. An Intimate Biography of his Californian Years*, San Francisco 1975.

V. *Sekundärliteratur*

a) Gesamtdarstellungen Steinbecks und des amerikanischen Romans bzw. Dramas.

Allen Walter, *Tradition und Dream: The English and American Novel from the Twenties to Our Time*, London 1964, bes. S. 161–166.

Benson, Jackson (Hrsg.), *The Short Novels of John Steinbeck: Critical Essays with a Checklist of Steinbeck Criticism*, Durham, N. C. 1990 (bes. S. 132–142).

Davis, Robert M., *Steinbeck: A Collection of Critical Essays*, Englewood Cliffs (N. J.) 1972, bes. S. 63–69.

Ditsky, John, *John Steinbeck and the Critics*, Rochester, N. Y. 2000.

Dusenberg, Winifred L.; *The Theme of Loneliness in Modern American Drama*, Gainesville 1960, bes. S. 45–50.

Fingerhuth, Frank, *John Steinbeck und John Dos Passos: »American tradition« und gesellschaftliche Wirklichkeit*, Hamburg 1981.

Fontenrose, Joseph, *John Steinbeck. An Introduction and Interpretation*, New York 1963, bes. S. 53–59.

French, Warren, *John Steinbeck*, New York 1961.

– *John Steinbeck's Fiction Revisited*, New York 1994.

Geismar, Maxwell, *Writers in Crisis*, Boston 1942, bes. S. 256–260.

Gray, James, *John Steinbeck*, Minneapolis 1971, bes. S. 21 f.

Hayashi, Tetsumaro (Hrsg.), *A Study Guide to John Steinbeck. A Handbook to his Major Works*, Metuchen (N.J.) 1974, bes. S. 129–154.

– (Hrsg.), *Steinbeck's Literary Dimension: A Guide to Comparative Studies*, Metuchen (N.J.) 1973.

– (Hrsg.), *Steinbeck and Hemingway: Dissertation Abstracts and Research Opportunities*, Metuchen (N.J.) 1980.

Krause, Sydney J.; »Steinbeck and Mark Twain«, in: *Steinbeck Quarterly* 6 (1973) S. 104–111.

Levant, Howard, *The Novels of John Steinbeck. A Critical Study*, Columbia (Mo.) 1974, bes. S. 130–144.

Liedloff, Helmut, *Steinbeck in German Translation. A Study of Translation Practices*, Carbondale 1965. [Geht nicht auf *Von Mäusen und Menschen* ein; die Ergebnisse sind jedoch übertragbar.]

Lisca, Peter, *John Steinbeck. Nature and Myth*, New York 1978, bes. S. 76–86.

– *The Wide World of John Steinbeck*, New York 1981, bes. S. 130–143.

Marks, Lester J., *Thematic Design in the Novels of John Steinbeck*, New York 1969, bes. S. 58–65.

Meyer, Michael J. (Hrsg.), *The betrayal of brotherhood in the work of John Steinbeck*, Lewiston, (N.Y.) 2000.

Moore, Harry T.; *The Novels of John Steinbeck. A First Critical Study*, Chicago 1939, bes. S. 47–53.

Noble, Donald R. (Hrsg.), *The Steinbeck Question: New Essays in Criticism*, Troy, (N.Y.) 1993.

Petersen Carol, *John Steinbeck*, Berlin 1972, bes. S. 26–29.

Rauter, H. R., *Bild und Symbol im Werke Steinbecks*, Diss. Köln 1960.

Schumann, Hildegard, *Zum Problem des kritischen Realismus bei John Steinbeck*, Halle (Saale) 1958.

Tedlock, E. W. jr. / Wicker, C. V. (Hrsg.), *Steinbeck and his Critics. A Record of Twenty-five Years*, Albuquerque 1957.

Watt, F. W., *John Steinbeck*, New York 1962.

Wilson, Edmund, *The Boys in the Back Room: Notes on Californian Novelists*, San Francisco 1941.

b) Einzeldarstellungen zu *Of Mice and Men*

Beatty, Sandra, »Steinbeck's Play-Women: A Study of Female Presence in *Of Mice and Men*, *Burning Bright*, *The Moon is Down*, and *Viva Zapata!*«, in: *Steinbeck's Women: Essays in Criticism*, hrsg. von T. Hayashi, Muncie (Ind.) 1979, S. 7–16.

Bellmann, S. I., »Control of Freedom in Steinbeck's *Of Mice and Men*«, in: *CEA Critic* 38 (1975) S. 25–27.

Davac, Lee, »Lennie as Christian in *Of Mice and Men*«, in: *Southwestern American Literature* 4 (1974) S. 87–91.

Ditsky, John, »Ritual Murder in Steinbeck's Dramas«, in: *Steinbeck Quarterly* 11 (1978) S. 72–76.

Ganapathy, R., »Steinbeck's *Of Mice and Men*: A Study in Lyricism through Primitivism«, in: *Literary Criterion* 5 (1962) S. 101–104.

Goldhurst, William, »*Of Mice and Men:* John Steinbeck's Parable of the Curse of Cain«, in: *Western American Literature* 6 (1971) S. 123–135. Wiederabgedr. in: Meyer (2000) [s. S. 147].

Gurko, L., »*Of Mice and Men:* Steinbeck as Manichean«, in: *University of Windsor Review* 8 (1973) S. 11–23.

Hadella, Charlotte C., *Of Mice and Men: a kinship of powerlessness*, New York 1995.

Hamaguchi, Osamu, »Idiot Lennie in *Of Mice and Men*«, in: *Chu-Shikoku Studies in American Literature* 11 (1975), nicht paginiert.

Handley, Graham, *Brodie's Notes on John Steinbeck's »Of Mice and Men« and »The Pearl«*, London 1977.

Hwang, Mei-shu, »*Of Mice and Men:* An Experimental Study of the Novel and the Play«, in: *Tam-kang Journal / Business, Engineering, Liberal Arts, and Science* 11 (1973) S. 225–240.

Lippman, Bertram, *Of Mice and Men. A Critical Commentary*, New York 1964.

Lisca, Peter, »Motif and Pattern in *Of Mice and Men*«, in: *Modern Fiction Studies* 2 (1956) S. 228–234.

Marsden, John L., »California Dreamin': The Significance of ›A Coupla Acres‹ in Steinbeck's *Of Mice and Men*«, in: *Western American Literature* 29.4 (Februar 1995), S. 291–297.

Matthews, David K., »Allegory and Determinism in Steinbeck's *Of Mice and Men*«, in Robert Stanton (Hrsg.), *An Introduction to Fiction*, New York 1965, S. 83–88.

McEntyre, Marilyn C., »*Of Mice and Men:* a story of innocence retained«, in: Meyer (2000), s. S. 147.

Schwerner, Armand, *John Steinbeck's »Of Mice and Men«*, New York 1965 (Monarch Notes).

Short, M. H., *A Stylistic Analysis of John Steinbeck's »Of Mice and Men«*, M. A. Thesis, University of Birmingham 1970. [Exposé in: *Steinbeck Quarterly* 5 (1972) S. 58.]

Shurgot, Michael W., »A Game of Cards in Steinbeck's *Of Mice and Men*«, in: *Steinbeck Quarterly* 15 (1982) S. 38–45.

Slater, John F., »Steinbeck's *Of Mice and Men* (Novel) (1937)«, in: *A Study Guide to Steinbeck: A Handbook to his Major Works*, hrsg. von T. Hayashi, Metuchen (N. J.) 1974, S. 129–154.

Spilka, Mark, »Of George and Lennie and Curley's Wife: Sweet Violence in Steinbeck's Eden«, in: *Modern Fiction Studies* 20 (1974) S. 169–179.

Steele, Joan, »A Century of Idiots: *Barnaby Rudge* and *Of Mice and Men*«, in: *Steinbeck Quarterly* 5 (1972) S. 8–17.

Yano, Shigeharu, »Love and Death in *Of Mice and Men*«, in: *Bulletin of Reitaku University* 24 (1977) S. 39–58.

Zeittafel zu Leben und Werk John Steinbecks

1902	Geburt am 27. Februar in Salinas (Kalifornien) als Sohn des Mühlenbesitzers und Schatzmeisters des Bezirks Monterey, John Ernest Steinbeck, und der Lehrerin Olive Hamilton Steinbeck.
1919	Abschlußprüfung nach mittelmäßiger Schullaufbahn an der Salinas High School.
1920–25	Sporadisches Studium an der Stanford University (Interesse vor allem an Meeresbiologie); viele Unterbrechungen durch Gelegenheitsarbeiten, so als Straßenbauarbeiter, Erntehelfer und Schiffsjunge; Hochschulabgang ohne Abschluß.
1925	Wechsel nach New York im November. Arbeit als Maurer und Verfasser vereinzelter Reportagen für die Zeitschrift *American*; materielle Durststrecke.
1926	Rückkehr nach Kalifornien; Gelegenheitsarbeiten und erste literarische Gehversuche.
1929	Veröffentlichung des ersten (erfolglosen) Romans *A Cup of Gold* als Ergebnis seiner Beschäftigung mit Thomas Malorys *Le Morte d'Arthur*.
1930	Heirat mit Carol Henning; Übersiedlung nach Pacific Grove, der Farm des Vaters; Bekanntschaft mit dem Meeresbiologen Edward F. Ricketts.
1932	Übersiedlung nach Los Angeles; Veröffentlichung des aus zwölf Kurzgeschichten gefügten Romans *The Pastures of Heaven*; Rückkehr nach Pacific Grove.
1933	Veröffentlichung von *To a God Unknown*.
1934	Tod der Mutter; O. Henry-Preis für die Kurzgeschichte »The Murder«.
1935	Veröffentlichung des aus siebzehn Episoden bestehenden Schelmenromans *Tortilla Flat*; Goldmedaille des Commonwealth Club of California für diesen Bestseller.

1936	Veröffentlichung des im Erntearbeitermilieu angesiedelten Streikromans *In Dubious Battle*; trotz – oder gerade wegen – der zwiespältigen Aufnahme internationale Popularität; weitere Medaille des Commonwealth Club; Übersiedlung nach Los Gatos (Kalifornien); Tod des Vaters; Veröffentlichung des Artikels »The Harvest Gypsies« (gemeint sind die wandernden Erntearbeiter) in den *San Francisco News*; Reise nach Mexiko.
1937	Veröffentlichung des bis dahin erfolgreichsten Werkes *Of Mice and Men* sowie der (vorerst dreiteiligen) Erzählung *The Red Pony* im Februar; im Frühjahr Aufenthalt in New York und Arbeit an der Theaterfassung von *Of Mice and Men*; im Mai Antritt einer Reise nach Europa; nach der Rückkehr Fertigstellung des Bühnenmanuskripts; im November Aufbruch nach Oklahoma, um sich dort wandernden Erntearbeitern anzuschließen und im darauffolgenden Jahr mit ihnen nach Kalifornien zu ziehen; am 23. November Uraufführung von *Of Mice and Men* am New Yorker Music Box Theater; Drama Critics' Circle Award.
1938	Veröffentlichung der Kurzgeschichtensammlung *The Long Valley* (die meisten der Geschichten waren seit 1933 bereits im *North American* erschienen).
1939	Weltruhm durch die Veröffentlichung von *The Grapes of Wrath* im April (neben *Gone with the Wind* größter Bucherfolg der dreißiger Jahre); American Booksellers' Award und Mitgliedschaft im National Institute of Arts and Letters; Empfang im Weißen Haus bei Präsident Roosevelt; im Herbst Aufbruch zu meeresbiologischer Expedition mit Ed Ricketts (bis April 1940).
1940	Pulitzer-Preis für *The Grapes of Wrath*; Verfilmung von *The Grapes of Wrath* und *Of Mice and Men*.
1941	Von Januar bis August gemeinsame Arbeit mit Ed

Ricketts an *Sea of Cortez*, einer wissenschaftlich-poetischen Aufarbeitung der Expedition.

1942	Scheidung von Carol Henning; Veröffentlichung von *Bombs Away*, einem journalistischen Buch über die Ausbildung der Air Force, und *The Moon is Down*.
1943	Heirat mit Gwyndolen Conger im März; Übersiedlung nach New York; Tätigkeit als Kriegskorrespondent in Europa (bis Oktober 1943).
1944	Geburt von Sohn Thom; Veröffentlichung von *Cannery Row*, einer Weiterführung von *Tortilla Flat*.
1945	Veröffentlichung der nunmehr vierteiligen Geschichte *The Red Pony* und der Parabel »The Pearl of the World« (letztere im *Woman's Home Companion*; in Buchform 1947 unter dem Titel *The Pearl*).
1946	Geburt von Sohn John Steinbeck IV.
1947	Veröffentlichung von *The Wayward Bus*; im Sommer Rußlandreise.
1948	Aufnahme in die American Academy of Letters; Scheidung von G. Conger; Veröffentlichung von *A Russian Journal*; Tod des Freundes Ed Ricketts; Verfilmung von *The Pearl* und *The Red Pony*.
1950	Mißerfolg am Broadway mit *Burning Bright*; Arbeit am Filmmanuskript zu *Viva Zapata!*; Heirat mit Elaine Scott; Wohnung im verhaßten New York.
1952	Veröffentlichung seines »literarischen Testaments«, des Epos *East of Eden*.
1954	Veröffentlichung des Romans *Sweet Thursday*, einer Wiederaufnahme von Motiven aus *Cannery Row*.
1955	Musicalfassung von *Sweet Thursday* unter dem Titel *Pipe Dream*; Verfilmung von *East of Eden*.
1957	Veröffentlichung von *The Short Reign of Pippin IV* (»Book of the Month«); Verfilmung von *The Wayward Bus*.

Nachwort

I

Of Mice and Men, die 1937 veröffentlichte »play-novelette«, wird oft (und manchmal fast im Sinne einer Trilogie) in eine Reihe gestellt mit den Romanen *In Dubious Battle* (1936), der Geschichte eines Streiks durch Wanderarbeiter auf kalifornischen Obstplantagen, und *The Grapes of Wrath* (1939), der Schilderung des Leidensweges der »Okies«, verarmter Kleinbauern aus Oklahoma, die in Kalifornien auf Arbeit hoffen. Diese Etikettierung ist irreführend, denn zum einen ist *Of Mice and Men* kein Roman (und sollte nie einer werden), zum anderen liegen die genannten Werke auch thematisch auf sehr unterschiedlichen Ebenen. Es erscheint daher sinnvoll, *Of Mice and Men* zunächst aus der Abgrenzung zu den beiden Romanen heraus zu charakterisieren.

Was auf den ersten Blick als einheitsstiftend erscheinen könnte, ist der gemeinsame soziale Ort, das Milieu der »itinerant farm hands« als einer sozial und wirtschaftlich, daher auch menschlich stark gefährdeten Gruppe. Während diese Gruppe sich jedoch in den beiden Romanen a l s G e s a m t h e i t durch ein Bewußtsein der Zusammengehörigkeit und der Solidarität, der Überlebensfähigkeit und der möglichen besseren Zukunft auszeichnet, ist dies in *Of Mice and Men* auf eine Zweierbeziehung ohne jegliche politische Einsicht beschränkt. Das Zusammengehörigkeitsgefühl der G r u p p e wird in *Of Mice and Men* ausdrücklich negiert, wird sogar in der Reduktion auf zwei Personen als unüblich erkannt.[1] Was die Überlebensfähigkeit betrifft, wird diese in *The Grapes of Wrath* in ausdrücklicher Absetzung vom »Klassenfeind« postuliert,[2]

---

1 Vgl. dazu Slims Äußerung: »›Ain't many guys travel round together [...]. Maybe ever'body in the whole damn world is scared of each other‹« (S. 48). Vgl. auch die Zweifel an der Rechtschaffenheit Georges, die vom Boss (S. 31) und von Crooks (S. 92) vorgebracht werden.

während George und Lennie sich in dieser Hinsicht von ihren eigenen Schicksalsgenossen abgrenzen: »[Guys like us] ain't got nothing to look ahead to. [. . .] With us it ain't like that. We got a future«« (S. 20). Gleichzeitig wird hier der Glaube an eine bessere Zukunft als ein individuell gehegter Glaube ausgewiesen, während Ma Joads Prophezeihung, »A different time's coming‹«, die Zukunft aller Okies meint. Bezeichnend ist in diesem Zusammenhang die Funktion der beiden oft als melodramatisch qualifizierten Schlußszenen der beiden Werke: Während Rosasharn Joad nach der Totgeburt ihres Kindes mit der nutzlos gewordenen Muttermilch die physische Existenz eines Verhungernden rettet und damit auch die Permanenz des geistigen Zusammenhalts der Gruppe symbolisiert, beendet George mit der physischen Existenz Lennies auch den Traum von der besseren persönlichen Zukunft.

Nun ist allerdings nicht allein die Beschränkung auf eine Zweierbeziehung entscheidend für den unterschiedlichen Aussagewert von *Of Mice and Men*. Die Paare von Führer und Geführtem spielen auch in den beiden Romanen ihre Rolle. Entscheidend ist die A r t dieser Beziehung. Das weitgehend isolierte Paar George und Lennie weist durchaus Bezüge auf zu der Christusfigur Jim Casey und seinem »Jünger« Tom Joad in *The Grapes of Wrath* bzw. den Streikorganisatoren Mac und Jim Nolan in *In Dubious Battle*. Doch Jim Casey und Jim Nolan, die auf ebenso gewaltsame Art ums Leben kommen wie Lennie, sterben im Dienst der Sache aller, gehen als eine Art Märtyrer in die Annalen der Bewegung ein, während Lennie an seiner mangelnden Integrierbarkeit in jedwede Gemeinschaft scheitert.

Diese ausgewählten Gesichtspunkte mögen genügen, um nicht nur eine gemeinsame thematische Darstellungsabsicht in den drei »proletarischen« Werken Steinbecks auszuschließen, sondern auch den Blick in eine lohnendere Richtung zu lenken. *Of*

2 Vgl. etwa Ma Joad: »Rich fellas come up an' die, and their kids ain't no good [vgl. Curley, Anm. d. Hrsg.], an' they die out. But, Tom, we keep a-comin«« (*The Grapes of Wrath*, New York [14]1968, S. 383).

Mice and Men scheint nämlich aus einer ganz anderen Schaffenssparte John Steinbecks erwachsen zu sein, den seit 1933 entstandenen und 1938 in dem Band *The Long Valley* veröffentlichten Kurzgeschichten.[3] In ihnen steht ebensowenig das soziale Engagement im Mittelpunkt der Intention wie in *Of Mice and Men*, vielmehr verlegt sich Steinbeck in ihnen nach bester Short-Story-Manier auf die Darstellung des (zwischen)menschlichen Bereichs, auf die Wiedergabe eines entscheidenden Augenblicks im Leben einer Person oder einer Personengruppe. Zwar hat sich in *Of Mice and Men* die Perspektive geändert: Im Mittelpunkt steht nicht mehr der kleine Farmer (wie in den meisten der Stories), sondern der seine Arbeitskraft an immer technisierter zu Werke gehende Großbauern verkaufende, wandernde Erntehelfer – doch weisen viele der Geschichten deutliche Parallelen in der Motivik, in den Handlungselementen und in den Figurenporträts auf.

So findet sich beispielsweise das Motiv des männlichen Partnerpaares auch in den Stories »The Raid« und »The Gift« (dem ersten Teil von *The Red Pony*), wobei ebenfalls einer der beiden die Funktion des Führens und der Instruktion übernimmt. Bezeichnend für den Ansatzpunkt der Kurzgeschichte ist jedoch die Tatsache, daß es sich sogar in »The Raid« (wo ein Neuling in die Methoden der Politisierung und Solidarisierung der Farmarbeiter eingewiesen werden soll) um eine psychologische und weniger um eine soziologische Fallstudie handelt.

Das Handlungselement des Rittes in die Stadt (um wiederum nur ein Beispiel zu nennen) tritt am vordergründigsten in »The Harness« zutage, ist aber in Variationen auch etwa in »The Flight« oder »The Murder« erkennbar. Peter Randall, der Protagonist in »The Harness«, reist einmal im Jahr nach San Francisco, um durch Trinken und Bordellbesuche der Bevormundung durch seine Frau zu entfliehen. (Im Fall der Farmarbeiter in *Of Mice and Men* tritt als Motiv zur Flucht vor der

---

3 In einer Biographie neueren Datums (*The True Adventures of John Steinbeck, Writer*, New York 1984, S. 325 f.) mutmaßt Benson, Steinbeck habe eine Geschichte für Kinder schreiben wollen. Dies erscheint jedoch sehr fraglich.

Einsamkeit unter Schicksalsgenossen ein nicht weiter reflektiertes Männlichkeitsgebaren.)

Am augenfälligsten sind Parallelen jedoch in der Figurentypisierung festzustellen, wie Steinbeck sie auch in *Of Mice and Men* anwendet. Da ist zunächst die Figur der frustrierten Farmersfrau, die sich ihre eigene (Traum-)Realität zu schaffen versucht: Die kinderlose und vernachlässigte Eliza Allen in »The Chrysanthemums« sublimiert ihren Mutterinstinkt in der Aufzucht von Chrysanthemen; die zu Kommunikation und Partnerschaft sehr bedingt fähige Jugoslawin Jenka Sepic in »The Murder« hält sich einen Liebhaber; Mary Teller in »The White Quail« kapselt sich ab und flüchtet sich in die Traumwelt eines idealen Gartens; Mrs. Randall in »The Harness« akzeptiert an der Realität nicht einmal die Gestalt ihres Mannes und zwingt ihn, ein Korsett zu tragen. Gemeinsam ist allen diesen »Korrekturen« der Realität ihr Scheitern: Eliza Allen findet die Chrysanthemen, die sie in dem Glauben, auf Verständnis zu stoßen, verschenkt hatte, am Straßenrand weggeworfen wieder; Jenkas Mann erschießt den Liebhaber; Mr Teller erschießt die weiße Wachtel; Mrs Randall stirbt und hinterläßt einen Mann, der weiterhin nach San Francisco fährt. Wenn auch in manchen der zitierten Fälle die Frau das Regiment führt, so reiht sich doch »Curley's wife« fast nahtlos als weitere Facette in den Reigen ein. Sie hat zwar unter der Dominanz des hysterischen Curley keine Möglichkeit, sich eine wirkliche Gegenwelt irgendeiner Art zu schaffen, aber sie flüchtet sich ebenso effizient in eine hypothetische Vergangenheit, der sie durch ihr »tart«-haftes Auftreten Glaubwürdigkeit zu verschaffen sucht. Wenn sie auch dadurch die von allen angeführten Frauengestalten am wenigsten rätselhaft wird, so leistet sie doch für die Komplexität der Handlung mehr als die anderen: Sie allein ist Sirene und Opfer zugleich – sie beschwört nicht nur Lennies, sondern auch ihr eigenes Ende herauf.

Doch nicht nur sie, sondern auch Lennie selbst ist in einer Vorstufe bereits in den Kurzgeschichten anzutreffen. Seine Rolle als »freak«, als »half-wit« ist, in anderem Kontext, angelegt in der Geschichte »Johnny Bear«, wobei der sprechende Name der Titelfigur bereits seine Beschreibungsmerkmale vorwegnimmt. Wie Lennie ist auch Johnny von der Realität wie durch eine Wand abgeschnitten. Sein überdurchschnittliches Gedächtnis für Gehörtes führt zu keinem größeren Verständnis der Wirklichkeit, sondern er gibt, ohne den Inhalt zu begreifen, für Whisky den Wortlaut belauschter Gespräche wieder. Seine Selbstmanifestation ist also ebenso unreflektiert und unbewußt wie die Lennies, dessen Bezug zur Realität ebenfalls fragmentarisch ist: er lebt, um seinen Streicheltrieb zu befriedigen.[4]

Damit führt Lennie am deutlichsten eine über die aufgelisteten Vordergründigkeiten hinausgehende Gemeinsamkeit der Kurzgeschichten in *Of Mice and Men* fort: die Unfähigkeit der Figuren »to control or even to understand their behavior.«[5] Daß diese Eigenschaft Lennies abgeschwächt auch die anderen Figuren betrifft, ja sogar die Haltung des Erzählers und darüber hinaus die Weltanschauung Steinbecks exemplifiziert, stellt eine Einheit her, die *Of Mice and Men* zu einer ganz besonderen Art von Kunstwerk werden läßt.

II

Durch seine Freundschaft mit dem Meeresbiologen Ed Ricketts gelangt John Steinbeck zur non-teleologischen Weltanschauung. Es ist dies eine Philosophie, welche die Bestimmung der Naturwirklichkeit durch Endzwecke verneint, welche also auch bestreiten würde, daß die Entwicklung des Menschen einem vorherbestimmten Ziel zustrebe.

Wichtig für die Betrachtung von *Of Mice and Men* ist dabei vor allem, daß Steinbeck diese Philosophie zur literarischen Methode macht, indem er davon absieht, »what could be, or should be, or might be,« sondern sich darauf beschränkt zu

---

4 Es wäre zu ergänzen, daß Merkmale, wie sie uns bei Lennie begegnen, auch in der Beschreibung der animalischen Sinnlichkeit der Lenka Sepic angelegt sind.
5 Warren French, *John Steinbeck*, New York 1961, S. 87.

sagen »what actually ›is‹.«[6] Oder, in anderen Worten, indem er versucht »at most to answer the sufficiently difficult questions w h a t or h o w, instead of w h y.«[7] Seixas weist darauf hin, daß gerade in diesem Sinne der ursprünglich vorgesehene Titel für *Of Mice and Men*, »Something that Happened«, seine wahre Tragweite erfährt.[8] Vor diesem Hintergrund ist auch mancher heftige Einwand gegen *Of Mice and Men* zu verstehen – und zu entkräften, z. B. der Vorwurf, Steinbeck präsentiere den Menschen quasi als Tier und dieses vornehmlich biologische Interesse verwässere seine Dichtung.[9] Dem steht natürlich die eigentliche Absicht gegenüber, »patterns of reality«[10] aufzuspüren und anzubieten, deren (falls vorhandenen) Sinn zu erschließen dem Leser vorbehalten bleibt.[11] Von daher wird auch sinnfällig, warum Steinbeck ursprünglich vorhatte, »Something that Happened« als Drama zu konzipieren:[12] Auf der Bühne läßt sich (zumindest scheinbare) Objektivität mit ungleich weniger Schwierigkeiten erzielen als durch das Medium eines Erzählers. Es sind wohl eher solche Überlegungen, die Steinbeck zu der Form der »play-novelette« führten, als jene, die er in einem Aufsatz des Jahres 1938 vorgibt.[13]

6 Zit. nach: Antonia Seixas, »John Steinbeck and the Non-Teleological Bus«, in: *Steinbeck and his Critics*, hrsg. von E.W. Tedlock, jr., und C.V. Wicker, Albuquerque 1957, S. 277.

7 Ebd.

8 Ebd., S. 276 f. (Vgl. auch den ersten Satz von »The Murder«: »This happened a number of years ago in Monterey County, in central California«.)

9 So John S. Kennedy in seinem Aufsatz »John Steinbeck: Life Affirmed and Dissolved«, in: Tedlock / Wicker (Hrsg.), S. 119–134.

10 Zit. nach: Seixas, S. 277.

11 Vgl. etwa Steinbecks Aussage, die Kurzgeschichte »The Snake« gebe eine tatsächliche Begebenheit wieder, »but he didn't know what it meant« (zit. nach: French, S. 87).

12 »I'm doing a play now,« schreibt Steinbeck im Februar 1935 an seine Agenten; zit. nach: Howard Levant, *The Novels of John Steinbeck. A Critical Study*, Columbia (Mo.) 1974, S. 133.

13 John Steinbeck, »... the novel might benefit by the discipline, the terseness ...«, in: *Stage* 15 (1938) S. 50 f.: Levant (Anm. 12) beschäftigt sich sehr kritisch mit den dort gemachten Aussagen, etwa, die »play-novelette« besitze eine rein dramatische Struktur (im bühnentechnischen Sinn), damit bei der Rezeption eine Art Gruppenerlebnis des Lesepublikums zustandekomme (*The Novels of John Steinbeck*, S. 130 f.).

Warum das Drama *Of Mice and Men* dann doch erst in zweiter Instanz als Bühnenbearbeitung der Novelle zustandekam, läßt sich im Zusammenhang mit der Änderung des Titels unschwer erahnen. Das »Something that Happened« zugrundegelegte »pattern of reality« muß sich unversehens als zu weitreichend erwiesen haben: Der vorliegende Text ist eben nicht nur eine zu lang geratene Kurzgeschichte oder Anekdote; zu deutlich sind parabelhafte Züge, als daß der Autor das stillschweigend hätte übergehen können.

Das »Wirklichkeitsmuster« wird vielmehr überlagert durch symbolische Muster, die über die Einzelbedeutsamkeit der Symbole in den Kurzgeschichten (etwa der Chrysanthemen oder der weißen Wachtel) weit hinausgehen. (Nun wäre das kein Grund, die Begebenheit nicht in Form eines Dramas vorzulegen, wäre nicht die Tatsache, daß Steinbeck in *Of Mice and Men* den Makrokosmos im Mikrokosmos unter Verwendung von Elementen abbildet, welche auf der Bühne nicht darzustellen sind, welche ihren Platz bestenfalls in einer Regieanweisung haben.[14])

Die Darstellung der Einsamkeit und Heimatlosigkeit der Wanderarbeiter wird zu einer parabelhaften Darstellung der metaphysischen Einsamkeit und Heimatlosigkeit des Menschen. Die Zufälligkeit dessen, was das Schicksal des Menschen bestimmt, findet ihre Abbildung in den Lebensvorgängen der Natur. So wie Lennie in Weed davonkommt, im Salinastal aber von seinem Schicksal[15] ereilt wird, so ist auch das Überleben oder Nichtüberleben der »water snake« (S. 12 bzw. 123 f.) ein Resultat des Zufalls, bzw. eine Frage der Zeit und der Umstände. So wie der Karpfen (S. 15) ans Licht kommt, nach Luft schnappt und wieder im geheimnisvollen Dunkel verschwindet, so erleben wir als Leser auch das Auftauchen

---

14 Vorerst seien nur als Beispiele erwähnt der Reiher und die Wasserschlange des Anfangs und Endes oder die gottähnlichen Züge, mit denen Slim ausgestattet ist (S. 46 f. und S. 54).

15 »Schicksal« ist hier nicht im metaphysischen Sinn zu verstehen, sondern als Produkt der Mechanismen der Lebensabläufe. Vgl. Steinbeck: »[...] whatever the modern word for fate is« (zit. nach: John H. Timmermann, *John Steinbeck's Fiction. The Aesthetics of the Road Taken*, Norman / London 1986, S. 98).

Lennies, der nach seinem Traum vom Frieden auf Erden schnappt, um dann von der Bildfläche zu verschwinden. Gott – oder ein göttlicher Heilsplan – bleibt indifferent im verborgenen. Seine Manifestation auf der Handlungsebene erfährt er im Wirken Slims, der nicht nach moralischen oder naturrechtlichen Prinzipien handelt, als er die Erschießung von Candys Hund absegnet, sondern nach den Erfordernissen des Augenblicks. Ebensowenig wird Lennies Totschlag nach den Prinzipien von Schuld oder Unschuld »gesühnt« (wie das beispielsweise im Fall von Curleys Hand die Situation erlaubte), vielmehr läßt die Augenblickskonstellation keine andere Lösung zu. Aus der Sicht von George (und das hat er aus dem Verhalten Candys während und nach der Exekution seines Hundes gelernt) besteht das kleinste Übel in der verantwortlichen Art, mit der er Lennie den vertretbarsten Tod ermöglicht. Es bleibt nur zu wiederholen, daß es sich hier nicht um schicksalhafte Verstrikkungen handelt, sondern um jeweils pragmatische Entscheidungen, deren ethischer Wert dahingestellt bleibt.

Um diesen zentralen Punkt zu verdeutlichen, daß Lennie kein Schicksal etwa im Sinne der griechischen Tragödie erleidet, sondern die partikuläre Konkretisierung von Allgemein-Menschlichem (wie auch sein Traum eine Art Menschheitstraum darstellt), unterlegt Steinbeck die Novelle mit symbolischen Bezugssystemen, die das Abstrahieren vom konkreten Handlungsverlauf erleichtern, ja erfordern.

Da ist zunächst das Gedicht »To a Mouse« von Robert Burns,[16] dem er den neuen Titel entnimmt. In ihm beklagt der Bauer, daß er unabsichtlich beim Pflügen die Lebensgrundlage einer Maus zerstört hat. Er beteuert, er würde willentlich nie Gewalt gegen die Maus ausüben, unterstreicht also die im System der sich überschneidenden Lebensbereiche angelegte Zufälligkeit seiner Tat. Andererseits bezieht er das »Schicksal« der Maus auf sich selbst, d. h. den Menschen, der sogar noch schlimmer zu tragen habe, da er nicht nur mit den augenblicklichen Unbillen des Lebens fertigwerden müsse, sondern bedau-

16 Vgl. die Anmerkung zum Titel, S. 140 f.

erlicherweise auch noch in der Lage sei, sich um die zukünftigen zu sorgen. Von daher betrachtet ist Lennie beides: Maus und Pflügender. Einerseits ist seine mangelnde Reflexionsfähigkeit dafür verantwortlich, daß die Seinsenklave, die er sich geschaffen hat (das zweckfreie Vermitteln von Zärtlichkeit), mit anderen, stärkeren Lebensbereichen kollidiert und daß seine Illusion von der Zukunft daran zerbricht. Andererseits bringt seine, ihm von der Natur verliehene, aber ebensowenig von ihm reflektierbare wie kontrollierbare Körperkraft den Mäusen, die er streicheln will, und in der Folge auch dem jungen Hund und »Curley's wife« den Tod. Darin liegt die wahre Ironie seiner Namensgebung, die Carlson im Scherz erahnt: er ist trotz seiner Körpergröße letztendlich erschreckend klein (S. 48). (Daher auch seine kindlichen Verhaltensweisen im Dialog mit George und in bedrohlichen Situationen.)

Zwei weitere Bezugssysteme sind, wenn auch als Kontrafakturen und daher weniger deutlich ausgeprägt, in *Of Mice and Men* eingearbeitet: die biblische Erzählung von Kain und Abel und die Suche nach dem Heiligen Gral aus dem Umkreis der Artussagen.

Lennie ist eine Art Abelfigur, die von der Rückkehr[17] ins Paradies träumt. George ist ein ins Gegenteil verkehrter Kain, der zwar die Realitäten der Welt nach dem Sündenfall, z. B. die Existenz von Gewalt, nicht in Abrede stellt (wie etwa Lennie, der nicht einmal seine eigene Gewalttätigkeit als solche zu erkennen vermag), der aber andererseits sich der Aufgabe, seines »Bruders Hüter« zu sein, nicht verweigert, diesen sogar in seinem Traum so gut er kann bestärkt. Auch er scheitert, auch ein wohlmeinender »Kain« kann den Gang der Schöpfung nicht beeinflussen. Er tötet seinen »Bruder«, wenn auch aus Liebe und Mitleid, nicht aus Haß und Neid.

Was die Gralssuche betrifft, wollen wir uns nicht in Spekulationen versteigen, als Denkanstoß sei jedoch darauf hingewiesen,

---

17 »Rückkehr« deshalb, weil die kleine Ranch die Wiederherstellung der Lebensumstände der Kindheit Lennies, zu Aunt Claras Lebzeiten, bedeuten würde.

daß man sehr wohl die Irrfahrt von George und Lennie als eine auf die moderne Zeit übertragene Inversion der abenteuerlichen Fahrten verschiedener Artusritter auslegen könnte, ebenso wie die kleine Ranch als sehr säkularisierte Form der Gralsburg mit Lennie als degeneriertem Gralskönig.[18] Daß vom Gral selbst dann nur die »dishes« übrigbleiben, die Candy waschen will, daß die von Lennie ersehnten »rabbits« zu den »pants rabbits« des »bunkhouse« verkommen, wäre allerdings eine sehr extreme Form von non-teleologischer Umdeutung.[19] Immerhin ergäbe sich, so man will, vielleicht die Parallele, daß auch Lancelot (mit »Lennie« als Verballhornung?) wegen seines Ehebruchs mit Guinevere, der Frau des Königs (»Curley's wife«?), des Grals nur im Traum ansichtig werden darf (vgl. Lennies Schlußvision vom überlebensgroßen Kaninchen). Aber hier stößt die solide Interpretationsarbeit an ihre Grenzen.

Kehren wir also, als letztem die konkrete Handlung übersteigendem Lesemodell, zu einem bodenständigeren Bezugssystem zurück. Wenn wir von Lennies (und Georges) Traum als sinnbildhaft für einen Menschheitstraum sprachen, ist das durchaus mit dem Hinweis auf die parabelhafte Offenheit der Novelle zu legitimieren. Auf dem Weg dorthin müssen wir aber Station machen bei dem Konzept des »American Dream«. Dieser so eng an den amerikanischen Westen gekoppelte Begriff ist zu komplex, um hier vollständig einbezogen zu werden. Deshalb sollen einige zentrale Begriffe, deren Wiederspiegelung und Brechung in *Of Mice and Men* sich fast von selbst ergibt, genügen. Lennies und Georges Traum läßt sich problemlos zum »homestead«-Bewußtsein in Beziehung setzen, zu einer Aufbruchsstimmung, die sich zur Pionierzeit aus Konzepten wie der uneingeschränkten persönlichen Freiheit,

18 So weithergeholt es zunächst auch scheinen mag, sind die Artussagen als Inspirationsquelle oder Handlungsmodell bei Steinbeck immer im Auge zu behalten, hat er sich doch nicht nur bis ins Alter mit ihnen beschäftigt, sondern auch seinen ersten Roman, *Cup of Gold*, nach Malorys Vorlage strukturiert.

19 Dem entspräche z. B. auch die dialektal eingefärbte, redensartliche Verwendung des Bibelzitats, welches das Gelobte Land verheißt: »Ye shall eat the fat of the land« (zum ersten Mal S. 21, Z. 13).

der Chancengleichheit, des »pursuit of happiness«, der »self-reliance« und des »survival of the fittest« legitimierte. Daß diese Konzepte nicht erst heute, sondern vor allem auch im Amerika nach 1929 ihre positiven Konnotationen sehr schnell verloren, bedarf keiner weiteren Erläuterung. Gerade das ursprünglich auch religiös verstandene »survival of the fittest« erwies sich sehr bald als unbarmherziges Prinzip der sozialen Selektion. Von daher betrachtet erscheint es schon fast tragikomisch, wenn eine Figur wie Lennie diese veralteten Konzepte für sich in Anspruch nimmt, anstatt wie Crooks und Candy stillschweigend zu resignieren. Daß das Resultat nur in der Negation dieses Traumes liegen kann, ist das mindeste an Realismus, das man von einem Autor der dreißiger Jahre erwarten muß. Aber, wie gesagt, wird diese Art des sozialen Realismus in *Of Mice and Men* relativiert, wenn nicht aufgehoben, durch andere Folien, die der Handlung unterlegt werden. Eine eindeutige Fixierung der Novelle auf ein Lesemodell und eine Interpretationsbasis verbietet sich. Wir kehren deshalb, nachdem wir verschiedene, ihre Bedeutung über die Handlung hinaus zur Allegorie erhebende Ansätze angedeutet haben, zum Text selbst zurück.

III

Es ist oft geschrieben worden, und wir haben dies soeben expliziert, daß *Of Mice and Men* auf verschiedenen Ebenen rezipiert werden kann,[20] insbesondere der non-teleologischen und der symbolischen. (Eine dritte Ebene, die des sozialen Protests, versuchten wir zu Beginn als eigenständiges Lesemodell auszuschließen.) Es bleibt eine vierte Ebene, die Textebene, und es wird sich zeigen, daß auch sie von beeindruckender Qualität ist und nachträglich den überwältigenden Publikumserfolg sowohl der Novelle als auch des Stücks rechtfertigt.

20 Vgl. Seixas, S. 276 f., oder Peter Lisca, »Motif and Pattern in *Of Mice and Men*«, in: Modern Fiction Studies 2 (1956) S. 232 f.

Die Makrostruktur von *Of Mice and Men* ist zyklisch angelegt, was das Sich-im-Kreise-Bewegen der Personen augenfällig unterstreicht. Bezieht man die Vorgeschichte mit ein, spannt sich ein großer Bogen von dem Vorfall in Weed und der anschließenden Verfolgung zum Tod von »Curley's wife« und dem Zur-Strecke-Bringen Lennies. Innerhalb dieses Steigerungsbogens bildet der Text selbst eine Kreisbewegung ab, die von der Lichtung am Fluß (I)[21] über das »bunkhouse« (II,III), den »harness room«, den Crooks bewohnt (IV) und den Stall (V) zurück zur Lichtung am Fluß führt (VI). Zusätzlich zum insgesamt parallelen Verlauf von I und VI werden Anfang und Ende von den Gabilan Mountains umrahmt, auf die sich jeweils Schritt für Schritt das Tageslicht zurückzieht, während es im Tal immer dunkler wird. Erzähltechnisch sehr geschickt läßt Steinbeck dabei den Blick einerseits (dem Licht folgend) immer höher wandern, während er andererseits nach Art der Zoom-Technik unten immer kleinere Details vermittelt. Diese Details tauchen zum großen Teil sowohl in I als auch in VI auf, vertiefen also zusammen mit der Parallelität der Handlungen und Dialoge zwischen George und Lennie die Stringenz des Kreisschlusses, der auf die Handlungsebene übertragen den Circulus vitiosus von Desillusionierung (über den Fehlschlag in Weed) und Neuaufbau der Illusion (durch Reinkantierung des Traums) in I über die schrittweise Demontage des neuen Anlaufs von II bis V zum schließlichen Eingeständnis des Scheiterns durch George in VI umfaßt. In diesen Handlungsverlauf ist zudem ein konzentrischer Kreis eingebaut, der ihn noch einmal im kleinen abbildet (IV): Die Szene in Crooks' Kammer beginnt damit, daß Crooks sich seinen verkrüppelten Rücken salbt; auf Lennies Traum reagiert er zunächst mit desillusionierenden Bemerkungen, um schließlich selbst davon gefangengenommen zu werden; als George (in diesem Fall die Außenwelt) in diese Idylle einbricht, begräbt Crooks seine Hoffnungen und kehrt zurück zu seiner anfänglichen Beschäf-

---

21 Die Numerierung mit römischen Ziffern entspricht im folgenden den Zahlwörtern als Kapitelüberschriften im Text.

tigung.[22] Allein diese groß angelegte Organisation der Erzählung vermittelt auf ästhetischer Ebene die Unausweichlichkeit des Endes.

Doch Steinbeck läßt es dabei nicht bewenden. Er strukturiert diesen großen Rahmen bis in die kleinste Einzelheit durch. Seine herausragenden Techniken sind dabei die Wiederholung, die Parallelisierung und die Kontrastierung. Die große Kreisbewegung ist durchzogen von kleineren Schleifenbildungen, die sich stetig wiederholen. So wird etwa die Einsamkeit der »ranch hands« fast wortgetreu immer wieder hervorgehoben (zunächst durch George, dann durch Slim, Candy und Crooks, in verwandter Form auch durch »Candy's wife«). Auffälligste Repetition ist allerdings das Ritual des Traumes von Freiheit und Gemeinschaft, welches George mit Lennie an allen Kernstellen zelebriert, welches aber auch Lennie, wenn er allein ist, reproduziert. Der Traum der beiden (eigentlich nur Lennies) verläßt dadurch die Ebene der Realisierbarkeit und wird zum liturgischen Versatzstück. Ebenso realitätsverfestigend (und damit traumfeindlich) wirken in ihrer Häufung das Patiencespiel Georges und der Ritt in Susys oder ein imaginiertes Bordell.

Wie diese Wiederholungen vertiefen Parallelszenen die Unmöglichkeit einer alternativen Lösung. Die erdrückte Maus der Eingangsszene steht als »Schablone« im Hintergrund, wenn Lennie den jungen Hund und schließlich »Curley's wife« tötet. Ähnliches gilt für das Zerquetschen von Curleys Hand (verdeutlicht durch die Wahl des Verbums »to flop«, S. 83 und 115). Ebenso parallel dazu wird das Schicksal der vom Reiher gefangenen Wasserschlange beschrieben (»waved frantically«, S. 124). Auf einer zweiten Schiene wird die Erschießung von Candys Hund mit der Erschießung Lennies verquickt, verstärkt durch die Aussagen Slims (»I wisht somebody'd shoot me if I get old an' a cripple«, S. 60) und Candys (»When they can me here I wisht somebody'd shoot me«, S. 79). Diese

22 Es muß jedoch angemerkt werden, daß trotz des verpuffenden Hoffnungsschimmers der störende Einfluß von »Curley's wife« kraft der gemeinschaftsstiftenden Wirkung des Traumes in diesem Abschnitt letztlich bedeutungslos bleibt.

Parallelismen sind aber nicht nur Mittel der Verdichtung der Aussage, sondern dienen in ihrer Abfolge vor allem dem sehr frühzeitig einsetzenden und sehr intensiven »foreshadowing« des Endes.

Um eine zu große Endlastigkeit und Einseitigkeit des Effekts zu vermeiden, baut Steinbeck im Zentrum der Novelle eine Gegenbewegung, eine Art retardierendes Moment ein. Das Ende von Abschnitt III und fast der gesamte Abschnitt IV treiben die scheinbar greifbar nahe Verwirklichung des Traumes von der eigenen Ranch voran, bis der Ausschluß Crooks' durch George das bevorstehende Ende dieser Hoffnung antizipiert.

Auch unscheinbarere Gegenbewegungen, Kontraste und Kontrapunkte balancieren die allgegenwärtige Ausweglosigkeit etwas aus. So erhält Georges Tat am Schluß durch die Kontrastierung mit Candys Verhalten seinem Hund gegenüber über ihre pessimistische Botschaft hinaus die positive Bedeutung humanitären Handelns. Auch Lennie wird nicht einseitig, also ausschließlich animalisch gezeichnet, sondern setzt durchaus menschlich wertvolle Akzente. Er durchbricht mit seiner naiven Unschuld die verhärteten Fronten des »bunkhouse«-Daseins; er läßt Candy noch einmal hoffen; er reißt für einen Augenblick Crooks aus seiner Isolation und nimmt damit sogar rassischen Schranken ihre Absolutheit; er läßt schließlich »Curley's wife« nicht nur als »tart«, sondern ebenfalls als leidende Kreatur sichtbar werden. Er selbst erweist sich durch seine Fähigkeit, einen Zukunftstraum zu verfolgen, bei aller Fehlerhaftigkeit im Kontrast zu Curley als im engsten Sinne durchaus »geistig« orientiertes Wesen. Man beachte auch die Art, wie Lennie – ironischerweise als alles zu spät ist – aus dem »pool« trinkt (S. 124) und sich auch ansonsten, ohne Anweisung, wie George in der Eingangsszene benimmt: Er ist nicht mehr der plump einhertapsende Bär des Beginns, sondern tritt »as silently as a creeping bear« auf.

Diese zuletzt angedeutete Ambivalenz im Gebrauch der Tiermetaphorik ist bezeichnend für die Ambivalenz der meisten Figuren überhaupt. Erscheinen Curley oder Carlson auf den ersten Blick als unreflektierte »hard-boiled men«, die in erster Linie durch das »one-two« bzw. die Luger charakterisiert sind, relativiert genaueres Hinsehen diesen Eindruck. Als Carlson Candys Hund zur Erschießung führt, zieht er die Leine »gently« (S. 64), entgegen seiner scheinbar dominierenden Schießwut, die er ja auch bei der Verfolgung Lennies an den Tag legt (es ist sicher kein Zufall, daß ihm die Luger dann nicht mehr zur Verfügung steht: »it's been took«, S. 122). Und als Curley seine Expertise zu Georges Gnadenschuß abgibt (S. 133), tut sogar er das »softly«. Auch der anfangs resignierte Candy spricht »softly«, als er über der toten Frau Curleys, die er ja so rigoros als »tart« klassifiziert hatte, sein »poor bastard« intoniert (S. 123). Und auch der durch lebenslange Zurücksetzung zynisch gewordene Crooks erwärmt sich trotz obsiegender Resignation für den Traum Lennies.

Die seelische Verkrüppelung dieser Männer wird durch Lennies Schicksal gelindert. Bei Crooks wird dies nur andeutungsweise sichtbar – seine Isolation ist durch die Hautfarbe noch verstärkt. Er ist bezeichnenderweise auch am Rücken verletzt, während die anderen durch das gemeinsame Leitmotiv der Hände verbunden sind.

Candy hatte resigniert nach dem Verlust seiner Hand – er sieht sich nicht mehr in der Lage, sein Schicksal in die Hände zu nehmen, bis Lennie ihn wachrüttelt. Erst dadurch wird er zeitweilig wieder zu einem vollwertigen Menschen. Curley lief, was menschliche Zuwendung betrifft, trotz – oder gerade wegen – seiner »handiness« (»Curley's pretty handy«, S. 36) mit einer Prothese durchs Leben: mit Vaseline hält er eine Hand »soft« für seine Frau. Erst der Verlust der Hand durch Lennie ermöglicht es ihm, seine Sinne »in h a n d enough« zu haben (S. 84, Hervorhebung vom Hrsg.), um eine Verhaltensänderung denkbar scheinen zu lassen. Lennie selbst zerbricht letztlich an der Insuffizienz seiner Hände, die anders reagieren als er will. Daß dies sinnbildhaft gemeint ist, zeigt seine Reaktion auf Georges Vorwurf, sein Reden habe fast die Anstellung gekostet: »Lennie stared hopelessly at his hands« (S. 32).

Auch George ist in diesem Sinne »einhändig«. Fehlt Lennie die nötige Selbstkontrolle, um den Traum zu verwirklichen, ist es bei George die innere Einstellung, die mangelnde Identifikationsbereitschaft mit dem Traum. Er spielt das Spiel vordergründig um Lennies willen, wobei Lennie ihm aber auch als willkommene (Selbst-)Rechtfertigung dient (vgl. das Gespräch mit Slim, S. 54, bzw. Georges ständiges Insistieren, er könne sein Leben »so easy« führen, z. B. S. 16). Daß dem so ist, verdeutlicht nichts augenfälliger als die Tatsache, daß er ständig »solitaire hands«(!) legt, statt die Gemeinschaftsspiele »euchre« oder »rummy« zu spielen.

Die tatsächliche oder übertragene Fehlfunktion der Hände dieser »ranch hands«(!) steht allegorisch für ihre menschliche Verkümmerung.

Dies gilt auch für »Curley's wife«, die ihren Finger (!) »all set on the trigger« hat (S. 68), ständig auf wie auch immer gemeinte Konfrontation aus ist. Aber auch sie trägt ambivalente Züge, denn auch George hat bei seiner letzten guten Tat für Lennie den Finger am Abzug (von ausgerechnet Carlsons Luger). Dementsprechend ist auch »Curley's wife« nicht nur Femme fatale, sondern gleichzeitig vom Leben übergangenes Opfer, das sich in einen Traum flüchtet. Ihre wahre Sehnsucht nach Liebe und Geborgenheit offenbart sie, als sie Lennie anvertraut, daß auch sie manchmal mit den Händen durch die eigenen weichen Haare streiche. Wenn sie daran stirbt, daß Lennie genau das tut, ist die Beendigung ihres Lebens nur sichtbarer Ausdruck dafür, daß sie nie eine Chance zu leben gehabt hat.

All diese verkorksten »Leben« sind mehr oder weniger das Resultat nie zustandegekommener Kommunikation (vgl. den Monologcharakter der Rede des Pflügenden in Burns' Gedicht, S. 140 ff.; vgl. auch den Brief, den »Curley's wife« nie erhält, S. 111). Curley kommuniziert weder mit seiner Frau noch mit den »hands«, und sogar zwischen Lennie und George ersetzt das Ritual die eigentliche Verständigung. Nicht zuletzt reden auch die beiden Opfer, Lennie und »Curley's wife«, in der Hauptsache aneinander vorbei. Nur mit Candy und – nach anfänglichen Schwierigkeiten – mit Crooks ergibt sich für Lennie eine ernsthafte Kommunikationsbasis, auch wenn sie dem Gang der Dinge nicht standhält.

Was letztlich bleibt, sind die oben genannten Signale von »softness« und »gentleness«, die Lennies Traum vom weichen Kaninchenfell nicht ganz so sinnlos erscheinen lassen, und die angedeutete Verständigung zwischen George und Slim. Die Verständnislosigkeit der Gruppe am Ende (»What the hell is eatin' them two guys?«, S. 133) zeigt zwar, daß das noch nicht sehr viel bedeutet, aber die – wenn auch noch so unscheinbaren – positiven Tendenzen lassen völlige Hoffnungslosigkeit auch nicht aufkommen. Doch das liegt wahrscheinlich schon gar nicht mehr in der Aussage a b s i c h t Steinbecks. Es mag im »pattern« von *Of Mice and Men* angelegt sein, es gibt aber auch andere Wege, dieses Muster bei der Rezeption neu zusammenzusetzen.

Reinhard Gratzke

Inhalt

Reclams Rote Reihe

Originaltexte fremdsprachiger Literatur

ENGLISCH FRANZÖSISCH SPANISCH ITALIENISCH RUSSISCH

Ungekürzt und unbearbeitet, mit der Übersetzung schwieriger Wörter auf jeder Seite und einem Nachwort mit Informationen zu Autor und Werk.

LATEIN

Die wichtigsten Werke der römischen Literatur in Auswahlausgaben und Textsammlungen zu verschiedenen Themenbereichen. Ein Kommentar am Fuß jeder Seite liefert die nötigen Sprach- und Sacherläuterungen.

Sprachtraining

Sprachen leichter lernen und Grammatikkenntnisse auffrischen mit den Sprachtrainingsbänden aus Reclams Roter Reihe.

Das komplette Programm und Detailinformationen zu jedem Titel recherchieren und bestellen unter
www.reclam.de

Reclam